THOSE REDCOAT MOUNTIES DON'T
KNOW WHAT'S HIT THEM WHEN
M*A*S*H* DESCENDS ON MONTREAL
WITH –

JOSEPHINE BURTON BABCOCK III
Her only son Bubba is the fruit of an all-too-
brief marriage and he's the apple of Josephine's
eye. And when 'Precious Babykins' sets his
heart on a 'big boobed blonde hussy' Mamma's
wrath sends her in hot pursuit across the border.

SCARLETT JONES
The hussy in question. She and 'Baby Bubba'
are dead set on tying the knot in Montreal.
After all, Hawkeye has advised them that, 'It's
better to marry than to burn!'

MS SYDNEY PRESCOTT
A purple-haired advertising whizz kid whose
imaginative genius sent sales of 'Old Billy Goat
Snuff' soaring. Her unique sales pitch consists
of just one line: 'Up yours, Sweetie!'

ESTHER FLANAGAN
Affectionately known as 'Red'. As Chief of
Nursing at Spruce Harbor Medical Centre she's
the 'best gas-passer around'. And her talents
are sorely tried when she is called to the rescue
in Montreal!

1

M*A*S*H
GOES TO MONTREAL

RICHARD HOOKER and
WILLIAM E. BUTTERWORTH

SPHERE BOOKS LIMITED
30/32 Gray's Inn Road, London WC1X 8JL

First published in Great Britain by Sphere Books Ltd 1979
Copyright © Richard Hornberger and
William E. Butterworth 1977

Set in Times

Printed in Great Britain by
William Collins Sons & Co Ltd
Glasgow

In fond memory of
Malcolm Reiss,
gentleman literary agent

June 3, 1905 – December 17, 1975

– Richard Hooker
and W. E. Butterworth

Chapter One

Hazel Heidenheimer (née Schultz), the chief telephone operator of the Spruce Harbor, Maine, Medical Centre, was seldom in the least excited by incoming calls to her switchboard. She had, after all, given what she thought of as 'the best years' of her life to Ma Bell before joining the Medical Centre staff. Furthermore, her marriage* to Arnold 'Ace' Heidenheimer, who was not only sergeant-at-arms of Louis T. Abromowitz Post 5660, VFW, but, professionally, international relations coordinator of the Spruce Harbor Telephone Company (dealing with the French-Canadian telephone people across the border in Canada), had conditioned her to receive all manner of calls, often at odd hours, which could be only described as 'unusual'.

But this call was something special. No sooner had Hazel announced: 'Spruce Harbor Medical Centre!' in her well-practised smiling voice and the caller had in reply announced: 'Dr Benjamin Franklin Pierce. FFF,** please. The Matthew Q. Framingham Foundation is

---

* It was her marriage to Ace, of course, that had brought her career with Ma Bell to a premature closing. So long as she had been, as her supervisor put it, 'just fooling around with Ace,' Ma Bell was willing to look the other way as indeed, it had been doing for fifteen years. But now that she had finally gotten Ace to the altar, things were changed. Whatever else Ma Bell could be accused of, and God knows how long that list is, nepotism was an absolute no-no. Hazel, still hardly more than a blushing bride, was, after a formal banquet at which she was presented with a certificate of appreciation, the best wishes of her co-workers, and the cushioned seat on which she had sat for eighteen years, given the old heave-ho by way of early retirement.

** Framingham Foundation Fellow.

calling,' than her heartbeat began to quicken.

While Dr Pierce, who was Spruce Harbor Medical Centre's chief of surgery, did, in fact, regularly receive odd telephone calls from all sorts of strange people, both personally and in his professional capacity, he rarely received a call from an organization of such prestigious reputation as the Framingham Foundation.

High on the list, a long list, of things that puzzled Hazel Heidenheimer about the Spruce Harbor Medical Centre and its staff was how Dr Pierce and his assistant and crony, John Francis Xavier McIntyre, MD, FACS, had even been selected for membership in the Framingham Foundation.

While she liked 'Hawkeye', as Dr Pierce was known by one and all, and 'Trapper John', as Dr McIntyre was similarly addressed, they were not, in Mrs Hazel Heidenheimer's private opinion, the sort of healers who were sought out by staid and dignified organizations of any kind.

It was only, Ace had confided to her in the privacy of their nuptial chamber, that both physicians were willing to treat, at no charge, and in absolute secrecy, their fellow comrades of Post 5660, VFW, who happened to be afflicted with certain social diseases that they had *not* been convicted of by a VFW court-martial for conduct unbecoming members of the VFW at the last state convention.

'What were they court-martialled for?' Hazel had naturally enquired.

'I'm not so sure I can tell you,' Ace had said.

'We're married now, Dummy,' Hazel had replied, fondly. 'You can tell me everything.' She paused, and then added: 'And you'd better.'

'They gave Stanley* and Moosenose** something that

---

* Ace Heidenheimer referred here to Stanley K. Warczinski, proprietor of Spruce Harbor's well-known nitery, the Bide-a-While Pool Hall, Ladies Served, Fresh Clams & Lobsters Daily Restaurant & Saloon, Inc. and a past senior vice commander of Post 5660.

** Bascomb J. 'Moosenose' Bartlett, the mayor of Spruce Harbor and chairman of the House Committee, Post 5660.

made them go blue.'

'You mean they were sad?'

'They were sad, all right. Moosenose was crying, but that's not what I mean.'

'What do you mean, darling?' she pursued.

'When I said it made them go blue, Hazel, I mean it *made them go blue*.'

'You mean they actually turned blue?'

'Not exactly, darling,' Ace had replied, his face contorted with embarrassment.

His bride could read his face like a road map. Realization, as they say, dawned. Hazel Heidenheimer giggled.

'It's not funny, Hazel,' Ace said loyally. 'If you had seen Moosenose's face when he came out of the men's room, you wouldn't be laughing like that.'

She laughed louder.

'If I had known about this sadistic streak of yours, Hazel, you'd still be giving out information,' Ace snapped. It had no effect. Hazel was convulsed and it was a good two minutes before it subsided and she could pursue the matter further.

'And they court-martialled them for that?' she asked.

'You bet they did! The VFW is a brotherhood of men who have shared the rigours of warfare on foreign soil. They're supposed to stick together, not scare hell out of each other. It's not like they had slipped that stuff into a legionnaire's drink. That would have been good clean fun. These were brother comrades of the VFW they done it to. Of course they were court-martialled!'

'But not convicted?'

'No, as a matter of fact, they were acquitted.'

'How come?'

'The VFW, Hazel, runs its courts-martial fair and square. And, besides, with the exception of Father O'Malley, everybody on the court had had, at one time or another . . . Hazel, married or not, that's all I'm going to say about this. We boys are entitled to our little secrets, too.'

He told her all, of course, before the little boudoir

9

chat was over. And the whole incident was just one more reason why Hazel Schultz Heidenheimer was surprised that both Dr Hawkeye Pierce and Dr Trapper John McIntyre were fellows of the Framingham Foundation. Despite her frankly unkind suspicions of what went on in any organization composed solely of male animals, she could not imagine any Framingham Fellow slipping something into the glass of another Framingham Fellow that would make him go blue.

But truth, as they say, being stranger than fiction, it was beyond question that both doctors were Framingham Fellows, and it was also true that when the call came from the Framingham Foundation for Dr Pierce that Dr Pierce was 'in conference', which posed certain other problems.

The conferences over which Dr Pierce presided were held in his office immediately following the last surgical procedure of the day. Dr McIntyre and Esther Flanagan, RN, who was both chief operating-room nurse and chief of nursing services, were sort of *ex officio* conference members, and faithfully attended each conference. From time to time, depending on the circumstances, others were in attendance. Anaesthesiologists, for example, and student nurses whom Esther Flanagan was trying to steer, career-wise, away from aspirin dispensing and into the operating room.

When a conference was in session, an illuminated sign above Dr Pierce's office door cleverly reading CONFERENCE IN SESSION was illuminated and, by depressing a button on his telephone, he could make a red light light up on Hazel's switchboard signifying the same thing.

Dr Pierce did not wish to be disturbed while in conference for anything short of a medical catastrophe, and grew quite disturbed if he was. One of the jolly legends of the Spruce Harbor Medical Centre was about the time Mr T. Alfred Crumley, the Medical Centre administrator, had violated a conference's privacy so that he could bring to Dr Pierce's attention his belief that the

Medical Centre was going to have a hard time collecting from one of Dr Pierce's patients. Dr Pierce and Dr McIntyre had assaulted Mr Crumley by knocking him down, firmly tying him up with adhesive tape, loading him upon a laundry cart and sending him merrily rolling through the Medical Centre parking lot.

A call from the Framingham Foundation was not, on its face, a medical catastrophe but, on the other hand, it could not be ignored either.

'Dr Pierce is in conference,' Hazel said. 'But . . .'

'In that event,' the clipped, precise tones of her counterpart at the Framingham Foundation's Cambridge, Massachusetts, headquarters said, 'the Framingham Foundation will speak to Dr John Francis Xavier McIntyre, FFF.'

'I'm afraid that Dr McIntyre is also in conference,' Hazel said. 'But I will tell him that you're calling.'

'One would certainly hope so,' the lady from the Framingham Foundation switchboard sniffed.

Steeling herself for the very real possibility of an explosion, Hazel pushed the button that caused the telephone on Dr Pierce's desk to ring.

'Answer that, Esther, will you?' Dr Pierce said. 'I've got two darts to go.'

In fact, his foot was stationed the required four inches behind the marking line and his right hand poised to send another feather-tailed missile towards the target.

The target was a photograph of an officer of the Army Medical Corps in what is known as a Class A uniform – that is, tunic, shirt, tie and brimmed cap. It was mounted on a corkboard, held in place by a series of concentric wire circles in the lines of a bull's eye. The centre of the target, the bull's-eye itself, was directly over the officer's nose.

The photograph was of Maj. Frank Burns, Medical Corps, US Army Reserve, with whom both Dr Pierce and Dr McIntyre had served in the 4077th Mobile Army Surgical Hospital (or, acronymically, MASH) during the

Korean War. Dr Pierce had obtained it from the army for just the purpose to which it was now being put.

(The army does not, as a general rule, offer photographs of officers to former servicemen for use as dart targets. The demand would be enormous, of course, and the army has other things to do. But, in this case, Dr Pierce was able to enlist the support of a very senior officer, Maj. General Henry Blake, Medical Corps,* who, upon learning what Dr Pierce intended to do with the photograph, personally called the chief signal officer of the army and, as a personal favour, asked him to ship a hundred copies of the photograph air mail special delivery.)

'Right in the left eye!' Dr Trapper John McIntyre called. 'Good show, Hawkeye!'

Dr Hawkeye Pierce smiled and bowed modestly. 'Practice makes perfect,' he said. Then he turned to look at Esther Flanagan, who was in the process of setting her martini glass down so that she could pick up the telephone.

'Office of the chief of surgery,' Nurse Flanagan said. 'Chief of Nursing services speaking.'

'Esther, Hazel,' Hazel said. 'The Framingham Foundation wants to speak to Hawkeye or, if not him, Trapper John. Can they be disturbed?'

'I'll ask,' Esther said. 'Hawkeye, do you want to talk to the Framingham Foundation?'

'Tell them I gave at the office,' Hawkeye said.

'What about you, Trapper John?' Esther asked.

'Shame on you, fellow!' Trapper John said to Hawkeye. 'When the Framingham Foundation calls a fellow, the least a Framingham Foundation Fellow can do is say,

* General Blake, as Colonel Blake, had been commanding officer of the 4077th MASH and knew Major Burns far better than he would have preferred. This is, of course, the same Col. Henry Blake whom certain sloppy chroniclers of the Korean War have erroneously reported killed in action. Harsh judgement of these people should be tempered with the awareness that writing is difficult indeed for the functionally illiterate.

"Howdy." ' He took the telephone from Esther Flanagan, and pushed the button that placed the call on the loudspeaker.

'Howdy!' Dr McIntyre said.

'The Framingham Foundation is calling for either Benjamin Franklin Pierce, MD, FFF, or John Francis Xavier McIntyre, MD, FFF. With whom am I speaking?'

'Three-F's McIntyre at your service, sweetie,' Trapper John said.

'One moment, please, Fellow McIntyre, for Mr Matthew Q. Framingham VI.'*

That luminary's voice came over the loudspeaker a moment later. He sounded like what he was, a six-foot-three, two-hundred-twenty-pound sixth-generation Harvard graduate and Boston Brahmin. In other words, he sounded like Elliot Richardson would if Mr Richardson talked twice as loud and two octaves lower.

'Matthew Q. Framingham VI here,' he said.

'Your dime, Matt,' Trapper John said.

'Trapper, dear chap,' Matthew Q. Framingham VI said, 'I had hoped to speak to Hawkeye . . .'

'He said he gave at the office, Matthew,' Trapper said. 'And so did I, if that's on your mind.'

'I daresay, old bean,' Matthew Q. Framingham said, 'that someone of your outstanding mental capacity, someone indeed who daily is required to call forth the most obscure minutiae from the dark recesses of his memory . . .'

'Put your hand on your wallet, Trapper,' Hawkeye called. 'I think I recognize the pitch . . .'

'Hawkeye, dear boy,' Matthew Q. Framingham responded. 'I was led to believe that you were unavailable.'

'If you've got money on your mind, Fatso, you better believe it,' Hawkeye replied.

'Put the vulgar subject of finance from your mind,'

* Mr Matthew Q. Framingham VI, great-grandson of the founder of the Framingham Foundation, serves as its executive secretary. A rather lengthy, but interesting, account of the foundation may be found in *M*A*S*H Goes to Las Vegas* (Sphere Books, London).

Matthew said. 'The Framingham Foundation is, I announce with more than small pleasure, at the moment both solvent and debt free.'

'How did that happen?' Hawkeye called, visibly surprised.

'One might say that much of the credit should go to the one under whose stewardship the foundation has been these past few years,' Matthew said. 'But to modestly turn aside any such response, I add that the last will and testament of the late Elwood T. Fosberry, FFF, has finally been adjudicated to be valid, and that we have received a small bequest, a very nice little bequest, to tell the truth, from the estate of the man known as the Canned Tomato Czar of the San Joachim Valley.'

'Can we spend tomato soup, Matt?' Hawkeye asked.

'The bequest was in the form of cash,' Matthew Q. Framingham said. One of Mr Framingham's problems, which is rather common among his peer group, is that he takes what other people say quite literally.

'I thought Fosberry died five years ago,' Trapper John replied.

'Indeed, he did,' Matthew said. 'Fellow Fosberry went to the Great Seminar in the Sky five years, two months and four days ago, to be precise.'

'Then why did it take so long to get the money?' Trapper asked.

'His widow and female offspring went to the courts in a rather shoddy attempt to have him declared *non compos mentis* and the will invalid,' Matthew Q. Framingham said.

'Why shoddy, Matthew?' Hawkeye asked.

'Her position was that any man who would leave the vast bulk of his estate to an organization that she described as "the last unashamed bastion of male chauvinism" was, *de facto*, *non compos mentis*. But she went too far. She also pleaded abject poverty. She and both daughters showed up in court wearing rags. I thought our cause, however noble, doomed for a while.'

14

'Why?'

'The probate judge was a woman,' Matthew said.

'Well, what happened?'

'The court held, in a brief summation, that the widow and the female offspring had enough money both to maintain their present life-style, that is to say, the three houses, the *pied-à-terre* in Paris, and one of the yachts, and to snare husbands for the daughters. And, so far as the charge of being *non compos mentis* was concerned, Her Honour held, that was patently absurd. Anyone who established in the same will a scholarship fund for the offspring of underpaid probate judges was not only quite *compos*, mentally speaking, but a splendid all-around chap who should be allowed to dispose of his hard-earned money in any way he saw fit.'

'And so we're flush?'

'In a manner of speaking, one might indeed say that.'

'What are you going to do with Fosberry's money?'

'Well, some of it will be applied to overdue bills, of course. We really dropped a bundle on the last seminar on "The Role of Religion in a Changing Society." Just between us, fellows, when Dr T. Mullins Yancey said that he was going to offer a programme on religious prostitution, I thought he was talking about coloured slides or, at most, motion pictures.'

'What did he do? I was in Texas, and didn't get to come.'

'Have you any idea what it costs to fly in twenty-five Indian hookers from New Delhi? First-class, too. One would think that as, so to speak, clergy persons, they would have been willing to ride tourist class.'

'Back to Fosberry's money, Matthew?'

'Oh, yes. Well, after we pay off some of the more pressing bills, we're going to redecorate the upstairs pocket billiard room. Put new felt and cushions on the tables, that sort of thing, and then re-do the walls so we hang the Fosberry Collection in a proper setting.'

'I'm not familiar with the Fosberry Collection,

15

Matthew,' Trapper said.

'Neither am I, but I was afraid to ask,' Hawkeye said.

'Your knowledge of fine art or, rather, the lack of it, never ceases to amaze and astound me,' Matthew Q. Framingham VI said. 'I suppose it's too much to hope that either of you have ever heard of the famous Frederick Remington oil – the one called "Encounter on the Plains"?'

'Is that the X-rated one? Where the Indian and the squaw . . .'

'That's the one,' Matthew said. 'Well, the Fosberry Collection is generally acknowledged to be the largest assemblage of *objets d'art* of that genre outside the Vatican. He left it to us, asking only that we mount a small plaque identifying the donor.'

'That certainly was very nice of him,' Trapper said.

'I have the artwork for the plaque right before me,' Matthew went on. 'It will be cast in bronze. Here it is. It will read: "Presented to the Framingham Foundation in Fond Memory of the Tomatoes I Have Known, by Elwood T. Fosberry, FFF." Now, isn't that touching?'

'Brings a tear to the eye,' Hawkeye said.

'And the upstairs pocket billiard room is just the place for it,' Trapper John said. 'The last time I saw ol' Fosberry, he was passed out on the bumper-pool table.'

'What's on your mind, Matthew?' Hawkeye said. 'I'm a busy man. Among other pressing matters, I've still got one dart to throw.'

'As I was starting to say to Trapper John,' Matthew said, 'I am confident that he and you, that is to say, the both of you, can readily recall, *verbatim*, that section of the oath you took upon being admitted as fellows.'

'Put your hand back on your wallet, Trapper,' Hawkeye said.

'Go on, Matthew,' Trapper John said. 'Carefully. You may be large, but there's two of us.'

'You swore, on your honour as gentlemen, to render

whatever aid and assistance it is within your power to offer, whenever such aid and assistance was requested by the widow of any Framingham Foundation Fellow.'

'You're asking us to render aid and assistance to the widow Fosberry? The same one that was trying to beat us out of the art collection and the bequest?'

'Not the widow Fosberry, actually,' Matthew said. 'The Framingham Foundation Fellow widow in question is the widow Babcock.'

'Never heard of her,' Trapper John said.

'Or of him, either,' Hawkeye said. 'Before our time, probably, Matthew.'

'That's odd,' Matthew said. 'You are obviously in error, for when I spoke with the widow Babcock just now, she specifically mentioned your names.'

'Never heard of her,' they repeated, in unison.

'But you do know the poor fatherless boy, of course, Burton Babcock IV?'

'Never heard of him, either,' they said, again in unison.

'The widow Babcock led me to believe that you had become friends in Texas. They call him "Bubba".'

'Oh-oh,' Hawkeye said.

'Oy, *vay iz mir*,' Trapper John said.

Chapter Two

The widow Babcock, Josephine Babcock cared for only two things in the whole wide world. At the top of the list, perhaps naturally, was Bubba, whom she thought of privately as my 'Precious Babykins.' Bubba was the only fruit of her too-brief marriage, and the apple of his mama's eye. Josephine Babcock devoted at least every other waking moment to worrying about her Precious Babykins and, now that Bubba was growing up, his future.

The world, Widow Babcock knew, was nothing but one snare after another for someone like Bubba, and what she was doing was simply her maternal duty, protecting her young from the lions and tigers and worse of the jungle of human experience.

In those moments when she wasn't thinking about Bubba, she thought of the one other thing in the whole wide world that she loved with a deep and unflinching loyalty. This was Burton Babcock & Company, Tobacco Manufacturers, of which she was chairperson of the board, presidentress and chief executive officer.

As the Annual Report to the Stockholders (which was thirty-eight pages long, printed in four colours on expensive paper and bound in Moroccan calf despite the fact that there were only two stockholders, Josephine and her Precious Babykins, each of whom owned exactly fifty percent of the 3,890,000 outstanding shares of stock*) put it, rather succinctly:

* Since the stock has never been traded, no New York big board price is available. Knowledgeable economists, however, and the

From humble beginnings circa 1750, Burton Babcock & Company has grown steadily over the years to become the fifth largest manufacturer of tobacco products for the consumer. In a vertically and laterally integrated corporate structure, Burton Babcock & Company presently manufactures seven brands of cigarettes, fourteen brands of cigars, five of chewing tobacco and four of snuff.

Seed from the B&B Seed Company is sown upon lands owned by the Babcock Land & Timber Company by farm vehicles specially designed and built by the Burton Tractor Works. Burton Babcock Farms, Inc. workers harvest the crops for processing in Burton Babcock & Company drying barns and final conversion into consumer products by the Burton Merchandising Company, Inc. Although the company's products may be found on grocers' shelves and in automatic vending machines around the world (many of the latter products are made by Burton Coin-Operated Machine Company), fully five percent are sold through the 605 familiar Old Burt Cigar & Tobacco Stores and the recent addition to our family of enterprises, the twenty-seven Now That You Are Where You Are, Baby, Booze and Butt Boutiques.

At the annual stockholders' meeting, held this year as always in corporate headquarters, the sixty-six story Burton Babcock Building in Babcock, Burton County, North Carolina, Mrs (Josephine) Burton Babcock III was unanimously re-elected as chairperson of the board, presidentress and chief executive officer. The board of directors, among other important business, passed a resolution welcoming Burton Babcock IV, who had been absent on military leave, back to his duties as special executive assistant to the chairperson.

Internal Revenue Service have estimated the value of one share of stock at figures ranging from $23\frac{1}{8}$ to $87\frac{7}{8}$.

Manifesting once again its unselfish interest in things of the spirit, the board authorized a grant to the Matthew Q. Framingham Theosophical Foundation of Cambridge, Massachusetts which, it is hoped, will enable that distinguished body to continue its good works for the general betterment of mankind. The grant was again made as a memorial to Burton Babcock III, FFF and former chairman of the board of Burton Babcock & Company, who was lost at sea in 1955.

For all of his life Precious Babykins had brought nothing but joy to his mama's heart, from the moment of his birth until last week, when Josephine Babcock sensed that the status quo was about to experience a severe upheaval, and if there was one thing Josephine Babcock didn't like, it was a change in the status quo.

It was whispered privately around Burton County, North Carolina that 'Josephine was not to the Cottage* born'. This was, of course, quite true in the literal sense. Josephine (Morgenblum) Babcock had come of poor but reasonably honest stock. Her grandfather, the late August Morgenblum had immigrated to the United States from his native Steinhager an der Donau (Danube) in the Austro-Hungarian province of Bohemia in April, 1914, three months before his regiment (the 17th Bohemian Light Horse, of which Herr Morgenblum was bandmaster) was called to the Imperial Colours for World War I.

Arriving in the United States with nothing but his wife, their first born, Max (Josephine's father), and his sousaphone, August Morgenblum had found employ-

---

* The Cottage was the Italian Renaissance family manse, whose tile roof covered, the last time someone counted, 128 rooms, which Burton Babcock, Sen. had built 1906-9, atop Mount Babcock. It had taken over a year to dynamite the four acres on which the Cottage sat out of the mountain, and two more years for a force of 125 workmen to build the Cottage. It has been described as 'one of the finest earlier examples of conspicuous consumption by one of the more important robber barons'.

ment quickly in New York City as a musician. Within a year, he had formed his own musical ensemble, Augie Morgenblum's Viennese Waltz Kings, and started out on the musical career he pursued for the rest of his life.

The one disappointment of Augie Morgenblum's life was that his firstborn, Max, was an absolute bust as a musician. He was, in fact, tone deaf. But he was a loving son and a hard worker and he had inherited from his mother an appreciation of fine food. By the time he reached manhood and took a bride, he was the acknowledged master of the Weiner schnitzel and the Sacher Torte as that art was practised in the Yorktown section of Manhatten.

As a wedding gift, August Morgenblum advanced his son the necessary funds to open his own restaurant and, had not the war clouds of 1941 lowered, Max Morgenblum would probably never have left New York City. In a burst of patriotic fervour, however (after all, the blood of the former bandmaster of the 17th Bohemian Light Horse did course through his veins), he closed the doors (forever, as it turned out) of Max Morgenblum's 86th Street Bierstube & Conditorei and enlisted in the US Army as a private.

This patriotic gesture nearly cost Max his happy marriage. As Brunhilde Morgenblum put it at that time, 'anybody who not only owns a successful restaurant but is draft exempt because of his wife and twelve-year-old daughter and who joins the army is out of his mind.'

In the first few weeks of his military service, Max often had occasion to reflect on his wife's point of view and to admit, in his secret heart of hearts, that there was, indeed, a good deal to be said for her position. But, while still in basic training at Fort Bragg, North Carolina, he came to the attention of the commanding general of the 82nd Airborne Division, who was making a routine inspection of troop messing facilities. The general, rather unaccustomed to *sauerbraten mit kartoffel knödel* followed by a *Demel Torte* cooked by a KP in a

21

mess tent,* was quick to recognize talent where he saw it, and to put it to use. Pvt. Max Morgenblum was soon Sergeant Morgenblum, the general's personal mess sergeant, and soon after that, when it occurred to the general that a unit about to fight the Dirty Hun could well use someone who spoke the language, Warrant Officer Morgenblum.

Brunhilde went back on her solemn vow *vis-à-vis* Max's military service** when *Life* magazine published a feature story of the 82nd Airborne Division training for war in North Carolina. Three factors arose when she read the article that caused her to reconsider her decision. One, there was a photograph in which Max appeared, standing to one side of the picture. He was far slimmer, she saw, than he had been since their honeymoon. In his officer's uniform, with the glistening jump boots (she was never to learn that it had taken three of the 82nd Division's largest MP's to push him five times out the door of the C-47 so that he would be a qualified parachutist) and the silver parachutist's wings, he was as handsome as she remembered him on their wedding day.

Factor two was the realization that since he was wearing jump wings and paratrooper boots he had, in fact, *ergo sum*, actually jumped out of an airplane in flight, to float to earth beneath a silk canopy. Damned fool or not, he was still her husband, and that sort of thing was obviously dangerous.

That he was still her husband, even if temporarily bereft of his senses, was also involved in factor three. The main character in the photograph from *Life* magazine was actually the general, welcoming to Fort Bragg

---

* Max had, in fact, brought his supper in a brown paper bag, aware that the menu of the day for that day was K ration, Type III (ham chunks in red-eye gravy).
** What she had said, specifically, was, 'It will be a cold day in hell, you overgrown adolescent, before I leave New York to go with you to the boondocks.'

the McSweeney sisters, the most popular singing trio of the day. As one of the McSweeney sisters (the redheaded one) shook the general's hand and smiled at the general, another of them (one of the blondes, that one with the larger mammary development) smiled at Max in what could only be considered a shameless leer of invitation and desire.

She went to August Morgenblum and tearfully laid her suspicions on 'Poppa Gus' ' shoulder.

'*Liebchen*,' the old gentleman said, 'dot's someting you've going to have to learn to live wit. Ve Morgenblum men haf a fatal attraction for duh ladies.'

That very day, having collected all the gas-ration coupons from everybody in Waltz Kings, Brunhilde set out for North Carolina in Poppa Gus' Packard limousine, with Karl-Heinz Hauptpferde, who played the French horn for the Viennese Waltz Kings, and whose son, Ferdinand was also in the 82nd Airborne Division.

On the outskirts of Fayetteville, North Carolina, they came upon a lady whose 1936 Ford coupe had broken down. As a Samaritan gesture, Brunhilde picked her up and offered to take her wherever she wanted to go.

'As a matter of fact,' the lady said, 'I'm on my way to Fort Bragg.'

'Isn't that a pleasant coincidence?' Brunhilde replied. 'So am I.' Feminine pride compelled her to add, 'My husband is *aide-de-camp* to the commanding general.'

'Isn't *that* interesting?' the lady replied. '*My* husband *is* the commanding general.'

'My boy Ferdinand,' Karl-Heinz chimed in, 'plays the bass drum in the division band.'

'And do you live at Fort Bragg with your husband?' Brunhilde asked, not knowing enough about the army to be awed by the general's wife.

'As of yesterday,' the lady replied.

'What happened yesterday?'

'*Life* magazine came,' the lady said. 'And I came to realize that if a trio of big-busted singers can make sacrifices for the war effort, so can I.'

And so began a lifelong friendship between the ladies. The general's wife was a North Carolinean, and when the division went overseas to war, she returned to her native Chapel Hill. At her suggestion, Brunhilde and Little Josephine went with her. They could give one another company while the men were away.

The second thing that Brunhilde said to Max when he returned from the war was that one thing Chapel Hill really needed was a Viennese Restaurant. He was doubtful at first, but Brunhilde's argument that Chapel Hill was a far, far better place to raise Little Josephine than New York City was unanswerable.

Morgenblum's Carolina Gasthaus (which included a cocktail lounge known as the Geronimo Landing Zone, Max having learned that booze is an inseparable part of the American cuisine) was a success from the moment the doors opened.

It was there, in the summer of 1952, that Josephine Morgenblum first saw Burton Babcock III. And it was there that Burton Babcock III first saw her. She was twenty, between her junior and senior years at the University of North Carolina, and helping her father out in Carolina Gasthaus by waiting on tables. In keeping with the ambiance of the establishment, the waitresses were dressed in quaint Austro-Hungarian native costumes, consisting of short skirts, knee-length stockings, embroidered aprons, dirndl blouses, with their hair braided and coiled in loops at the ears.

The moment Josephine saw him, she felt her heart go all aflutter, even though her professional restauranteur's eye told her that the handsome chap in the paratrooper uniform had drunk far too long and well from the neck of the bottle of bourbon he clutched in his right hand. She remembered, exactly, the very first words he ever said in her hearing. Raising the bottle in her general direction, he said to the two paratroopers with him:

'Screw Mom's apple pie. *That's* what *I've* been fighting

24

for. A big-boobed blonde in a low-cut dress!'

He said this loudly enough to attract the attention of Max Morgenblum. While Max absolutely forbade intoxication on the premises, and while he had been known to chase more than one of Josephine's suitors with a meat cleaver, the young paratrooper before him posed something of a problem. Here was a wounded hero (Max recognized the Silver Star and the Purple Heart ribbons) fresh from the Korean War, and wearing the beloved insignia of Max's own beloved 82nd Division.

Her concern for her father's reaction immediately became a moot point.

Holding the bottle on high, the paratrooper said, 'Don't go away, honey, I think I love you!' and then crashed to the floor.

Max Morgenblum quickly ordered that the young paratrooper be put to bed in one of the rooms of the Morgenblum Mountain Chalet Motel, and then had a heart-to-heart talk with his daughter.

'You must not judge that young man too harshly, *liebchen*. He has just come from the war. His friends tell me that he was given a battlefield commission. And he's a paratrooper. As I've told you before, *liebchen*, we paratroopers are not like other people.'

Josephine had nodded her head and blushed furiously.

'*Liebchen*, don't blush,' Max said. 'He said . . . what he said . . . as a compliment.'

'Oh, I know Poppa!' Josephine had replied. 'Poppa, you told me, when I was just a little girl, that when Mr Right came along, I would hear the sound of heavenly music . . .'

'Maybe a little Strauss,' Max said. 'So?'

'So I heard it, Poppa, the moment I saw that young man. Even before he said what he said.'

Max Morgenblum questioned her carefully, to make sure that she was certain, and then made his decision.

'In that case, *liebchen*,' he said, 'we'll have to make sure that he don't get away. Good paratroopers are hard

25

to find. If things go all right, I'll start him out in the kitchen, and he can work his way up to a position where I can turn the business over to him.'

'Oh, Poppa,' she said, and hugged and kissed him.

And so it came to pass that when 2nd Lt. Burton Babcock III woke up the next morning, he saw the smiling face of Josephine Morgenblum looking down at him. Over her shoulder, he saw the benign face of her father.

'How do you feel?' Josephine asked. 'Did you mean what you said last night?'

'What did I say last night?' he replied. 'We're not married or anything, are we?'

'Not yet,' Josephine said.

He looked at her suspiciously. 'Why would you want to marry me?' he asked.

She blushed. He blushed. Their minds, he realized, if nothing else, ran along parallel paths.

'But you don't know anything about me,' he said. 'I may not have a dime to my name.'

'Poppa will give you a job in the kitchen to start out,' Josephine said.

'Why should he do that?'

'We ol' troopers got to stick together,' Max said, and began to sing 'Blood on the Risers', which is the unofficial anthem of the 82nd Airborne Division.

'You're a former member of the 82nd Airborne All-American Division?'

'You bet your . . . elbow I am,' Max said proudly.

'You'd let your beautiful daughter marry a stranger, a penniless stranger, simply because he happened to be a paratrooper of the 82nd Airborne Division?'

'What else do I need to know about you?' Max said, deprecatingly.

'In that case, I accept,' 2nd Lt. Burton Babcock said, raising his head to be kissed.

'That can come later,' Josephine replied, averting her head. 'Your breath would stop a clock.'

'I'll call Chappie Wood right now,' Max Morgenblum said.

'Chappie Wood, the legendary Reverend George Wood, DD, wartime chaplain of the 82nd Division?' Burton Babcock asked, in awe. 'The chaplain's chaplain?'

'Certainly,' Max said. 'Nothing is too good for my little Josephine.'

Six hours after Josephine Morgenblum had been joined in holy wedlock to 2nd Lt. Burton Babcock by the Reverend Dr Wood, the bride called her father from the nuptial chamber.

'Poppa, have I got news for you!' Josephine said. 'Good news.'

'Good news? How can you tell so soon?'

'Poppa, you'll never guess where I am!'

'I'm afraid to ask,' Max replied.

'The Presidential Suite of the Carolina Ritz-Biltmore,' Josephine said.

'The nation's most exclusive and expensive resort hotel!'

'When I slipped him a hundred bucks for the honeymoon,' Max replied a little sadly, 'I didn't think he'd blow the whole thing in one night.'

'You can't rent a closet for a hundred bucks a night in this place,' Josephine said.

'What are you trying to tell me, *liebchen*? You're not married six hours and already I should send you money?'

'Burton owns it, Poppa!'

'Owns it? Owns it? Don't be silly. Everyone knows that the Carolina Ritz-Biltmore is owned by Southern Hotels, Inc., which is in turn owned by Babcock Land & Timber . . . He's *that* Burton Babcock III?'

'You got it, Poppa,' Josephine said. 'How many Burton Babcock III's do you think there are?'

'That's what happens when a girl trusts her father,' Max had replied, with satisfaction.

'I gotta go, Poppa,' Josephine had replied. 'The

waiters are starting to bring in the caviar and the champagne. Burton Darling tells me it's very difficult to have it flown in on such short notice from Iran.'

The union, which Josephine thought of as short but blissful, was shortly (fourteen months) afterward blessed with fruit, specifically a bouncing eight-pound fourteen-ounce boy named Burton Babcock IV.

And a year after that, Burton Babcock III was swept overboard to an untimely watery grave from his racing yacht, the 168-foot *Josephine*, thirty miles off Bermuda. Josephine refused to pay any attention at all to the nasty stories circulated that her husband had been in his cups at the time. Certainly, she should know far better than anyone that Burton sailed better drunk than anyone else could sober, and that if he went over the side, he'd been caught by a wave, or knocked overboard by the boom. Booze had nothing to do with it.

At the reading of the will it came out that he had left the entire estate, less a minor ($250,000) bequest to the Framingham Theosophical Foundation of which he had been a fellow, to his wife and child.

She saw it then, at that moment, that her divine destiny in life was not only to raise her poor fatherless child as his father would have wished him raised (with certain obvious exceptions) but to assume herself the full responsibility for the Burton Babcock & Company corporate empire.

She acceded to the posts of chairperson of the board and presidentress immediately and divided her life from that moment between raising Precious Babykins and running the affairs of the company. The idea of remarriage never entered her head. After her beloved Burton, it would have been anticlimatic.

Chapter Three

Precious Babykins (known generally as Bubba) grew up as normally as could be expected under the circumstances. Like his grandfather and his father before him, that is to say, against the violent objections of his family, he enlisted in the army and, in due time, earned the coveted wings and shiny boots of the paratrooper.

But there the similarity ended. Grandfather Max, it will be remembered, had to be physically pushed out of the C-47 aircraft whenever a jump was required. Burton Babcock III, were the truth known, had volunteered for the airborne forces in the belief he was applying for transfer to the air force. His distinguished service with the 508th Airborne Regimental Combat Team in Korea had been a result of his signing what he thought at the time was a request for relief from parachute duty. Despite a general belief that he was referring to the North Korean enemy when he made the often-quoted remark on waking up in the 4077th MASH following his being wounded, 'Thank God, I'm alive; now I can kill the bastards,' he was in fact referring to the officers who had led him to believe he would shortly be transferred to the air force.

Bubba, on the other hand, since the age of seven, had wanted nothing more out of life but to float godlike from the heavens under a nylon canopy. He had gone with his mother, at that tender age, to Fort Bragg for the unveiling of the 2nd Lt. Burton Babcock III Memorial*,

* The 2nd Lt. Burton Babcock III Memorial, located at the intersection of Smoke Bomb Hill Avenue and Division Avenue at Fort

29

and there had been, to mark the occasion, a demonstration parachute jump.

He went to parachute school at Fort Benning, Georgia immediately after basic training and was three weeks later graduated summa cum laude from that hallowed institution. He applied for and was accepted by Special Forces, and spent the balance of his enlistment as a Green Beret HALO technician, a period he was evermore to remember as the happiest of his life.

HALO is another of the army's little acronyms, standing for High Altitude, Low Opening, and it refers to the parachute technique of jumping out of an airplane at a high altitude (thirty thousand feet and more) and falling like a stone to a low altitude (one thousand feet or so) before opening the parachute.

'Mama,' Bubba had said to his mother on his first leave, 'there is no feeling in the world that can possibly compare with falling twenty-nine thousand feet like a rock through God's fresh air!'

'I'm sure there isn't, Precious Babykins . . .'

'I've asked you not to call me that any more, Mama. I'm a Green Beret HALO technician now, and Precious Babykins is very inappropriate, to say the least.'

'I'll try to remember, dear,' she said. 'What I was about to say was that while I'm sure falling like a rock, as you say, is a truly exhilarating experience, I hope you'll believe your mother when she tells you there are certain other physical sensations with which, when you're a little older, you will become familiar, which will please you even more.'

'You are speaking, Mother, I gather, of girls? Or, to be somewhat less than tactful, of the physical relationship between men and women?'

Bragg, is a larger-than-life-sized bronze statue executed by Gugliemo Gugliemi, the sculptor. It shows the bandaged hero, his head swathed in bandages, a .30-calibre carbine in one hand, a bayonet in the other, rising from a hospital bed. On a bronze plaque mounted on the Canberra-marble base of the statue are cast his immortal words, 'Now I can kill the [expletive deleted].'

'As a matter of fact, Prec . . . dear, I *was* thinking somewhat along those lines. You're getting to be a big boy now . . .'*

'Mother, to spare you any further embarrassment let me state succinctly that, as a Green Beret, I am not entirely unaware of the desires of the opposite gender. Our motto, as you know, is "*De Oppresso Liber*" which, roughly translated, means "To Free the Oppressed." And we take it very seriously. Every Wednesday night, and every other Saturday night, girls are bussed in from Fayetteville and, on a roster basis, we men of the Green Berets take turns freeing them of their oppressions. While I have found one or two of these encounters not entirely unpleasant, let me assure you that it can't compare with falling like a rock from thirty thousand feet.'

'One day,' she said, 'believe me, Precious Babykins, you will hear the sound of heavenly music, signifying that Miss Right has come along, and then you're just not going to care about your parachute any longer.'

'Fat chance!' Bubba had replied, and changed the subject.

Josephine hoped, of course, that when his enlistment was over, and he came home, he would be ready not only to assume his proper role in the Burton Babcock & Company corporate structure, but to give up what she privately thought of as his damn fool parachuting. She was to be disappointed on both counts. Bubba returned from military service with the announcement that he had, indeed, as the recruiting sergeant had promised, seen the whole wide world, and having seen it once, wished to see it no more.

'I have learned to appreciate the simple things in life, Mama,' he said. 'To identify that which is important, and that which is not. I intend to become a simple and

---

* Bubba had been getting to be a big boy for some time now. When this conversation took place, he was nineteen years old. He was then six-foot-three, weighed 215 pounds, and had a forty-eight-inch chest.

31

happy tiller of the soil, more specifically, to devote my life to the oldest of the noble pursuits, animal husbandry.'

'You want to race horses?' she asked. 'Why not? We own a couple of hundred thousand acres in Kentucky, and I'm sure that by asking around, we can find someone who would be delighted to see that you get started on the right foot. If you'd like, Precious Babykins, Mama will buy you Churchill Downs as a welcome-home present.'

'What I'm going to do, Mother,' he said, rather coldly, 'is raise pigs right here in North Carolina.'

'Pigs?'

'They're quite bright, you know. Far smarter than dogs. And horses, Mother, are rather far down the list, intelligence-wise.'

'Your mother wants you to be happy, dear,' Josephine said, biting off the reply that came to her lips. 'If you think you'll be happy raising pigs, well, then raise pigs and be happy.'

'I'm glad you understand, Mother,' he said.

'And I'm sure that you will find pig raising every bit as satisfying as you did jumping out of airplanes,' she added.

'You used the past tense, Mama,' Bubba had replied. 'Indicating your erroneous supposition that I have given up parachuting.'

'But you have, haven't you? I mean, you're out of the army now.'

'I'm surprised that you could even raise the question,' he said. 'I am, after all, the son of 2nd Lt. Burton Babcock III. I'm in the Reserve, of course, and will maintain jump proficiency. That's why I intend to raise my pigs here in North Carolina. It's so conveniently close to Fort Bragg.'

'I suppose it's too much to hope for,' Josephine replied. 'But you haven't heard any strange music lately, have you? Heavenly music, perhaps?'

'You're not going to start that nonsense again, are you, Mama?' he replied. 'I'm far too young to think of

32

marriage, and if you will excuse my indelicate language, I am sick and tired of being nothing but a sex object, from whom women want just one thing, without considering my desires and hungers. It's getting so that someone like me can't even go to the beach without being whistled at and, yes, even pawed, by hordes of shameless females.'

'Your father had the same problem, Bubba,' she said. 'You'll just have to learn to live with it.'

Josephine told herself that his disinterest in the gentle sex was probably a good thing. For one thing, the world *was* full of young women who would like nothing better than to get their hands on the Babcock fortune, not to mention Bubba Babcock, and it was entirely possible that she could sort of steer the right kind of girl at him when the time came. And Bubba was right about that, too. The time had not yet come; she was far too young to be a grandmother.

She did her best over the next year to keep Bubba aware of what was happening in the executive suite but, with one exception, he displayed a near-total lack of interest. He cared only for his pigs and for his week-ends, which he passed at Fort Bragg jumping out of airplanes.

The one exception, the one thing in which Bubba showed any interest at all, was what Josephine thought of privately as the goddamned bean, and which is known biologically as *soja hispida Babcockisis*.

The government, of course, was responsible for the problem. It had once again stuck its nose into the free enterprise system, trying yet again to throttle it on the altar of consumerism.

Soja hispida Babcockisis, a variant of the common soybean, had been around as long as the tobacco plant itself. It was not, as the government insisted, a 'noxious weed'. The proof of that was obvious. Herbicides that would kill it would also kill tobacco plants, which, in a sense, was the root of the problem.

Soja hispida Babcockisis grew, prospered, wherever

tobacco plants grew and prospered. For two hundred years, Burton Babcock & Company (and its predecessors) had, in fact, considered it as sort of tobacco. Without one word of complaint from smokers, the centuries-long tradition had been to simply grind it up and otherwise process it with the tobacco and forget it.

Josephine Babcock, who prided herself on her fairness, was perfectly willing to admit that she (that is to say, Burton Babcock & Company) and just about everyone else in the tobacco industry had gone a little too far *vis-à-vis* their interpretation of exactly what constituted tobacco.

There is more to the tobacco plant than the leaves, just as there is more to the corn plant than those succulent little kernels. Tracing what had happened was simplicity itself and, God knows, the corn processors had done it long before the tobacco people had. They had set the example by chopping up the whole corn plant, stalk, leaves, shuck and ears, and feeding it to cattle. It obviously hadn't hurt the cattle one little bit.

With that example before them, the tobacco industry could hardly be blamed for doing the same thing to the tobacco plant. Certainly, as Josephine frequently pointed out, since the ultimate consumer was going to set it on fire rather than eat it, the potential for harm was even lower. What had happened was that first the fibrous centre of the tobacco leaf, which had at one time been cut out and discarded, was roasted, toasted and otherwise processed along with the leaf itself. From that it had been a natural evolutionary step to include the branches and, ultimately, the stalk itself.

They had gone a little too far, as Josephine was perfectly willing to admit, when, rather than cutting the plant off at the ground level, they had started to pull the plant up by the roots and grind up the roots along with everything else.

Some trouble making busybody* had gone to Con-

* Specifically, one Hortense Quattlebaum, PhD, who, it turned

34

gress, where bleeding-heart Liberals and Socialists, just looking for a cause, had made a lot of noise about it. The tobacco industry, under Josephine's leadership, had been quick and above board to admit their error, and to take whatever steps were necessary to make things right. Josephine Babcock herself had composed the disclaimer, 'These cigars are predominantly natural tobacco, with non-tobacco ingredients added.'

Nothing, certainly, could be fairer than that. Even before the Supreme Court order, all cigar boxes of the Burton Babcock & Company had carried that warning, in letters a full three-eighths of an inch high, right across the bottom of the box where everybody who turned the box over couldn't help but see it.

(Since *cigarette* packages already carried the message, 'Warning: The Surgeon General Has Determined That Cigarette Smoking Is Dangerous to Your Health,' there seemed to be no point in putting anything else on cigarette packages, and the non-tobacco-ingredients statement had been left off.)

As any fair-minded person would have to agree, this was meeting the government's snoopers and do-gooders more than halfway. But, like the camel sticking his nose under a tent flap, once the bureaucrats got started, there was no stopping them.

At God alone knows what cost to the taxpayer, a legion of government snoopers went to work, analysing everything in a cigar. They detected the presence of *soja hispida Babcockisis* which, since it constituted about ten percent of the stuffing in cigars and cigarettes, could hardly be called brilliant detective work.

Not content with that, government snoopers then analysed *soja hispida Babcockisis* itself. They determined that it was a variant of the common soybean (the tobacco industry could have told them this, had they asked, and saved the taxpayers a large bundle of money) differing

out, wasn't even a smoker herself, although she admitted taking a little sniff of snuff on occasion.

from the soybean only in that when it burned, a peculiar chemical reaction took place, making the gases generated virtually identical to those gases one sees coming from jet aircraft during landing and takeoff procedures.

For some reason, while it was apparently perfectly all right for the airlines to spew thousands of cubic feet of these gases into the atmosphere day after day, the .3 cubic feet of gas in each cigarette and the 1.5 cubic feet in the average cigar* represented, according to the Secretary of Health, Education and Welfare, 'a clear and present danger to human life.' An executive order was issued by the president himself, on television, forbidding any further inclusion of *soja hispida Babcockisis* in any form whatsoever in any tobacco product whatsoever.

As someone who prided herself in obeying the law of the land, even when that law was clearly a gross miscarriage of justice promulgated by dictatorial fiat by a president who would never get another dime out of her, Josephine issued the necessary orders to have *soja hispida Babcockisis* separated from the other cigar and cigarette ingredients.

'Burn it!' she ordered, when her senior vice president, Ingredients, enquired as to Madame Chairperson's intentions regarding the separated bean.

She wasn't even permitted to do that. 'That traitor to his heritage in the White House,' as Josephine referred to our nation's maximum leader, issued yet another executive order. Citing as his reasons that smoke from the huge piles of burning *soja hispida Babcockisis* had not only seriously restricted visibility on the ground all over North and South Carolina, and as far north as Petersburg, Virginia, but had made people sick to their stomachs as far away from the burning site as Winston-Salem, North Carolina, Nashville, Tennessee, Savannah, Georgia, and aboard the SS *Charles E. Whaley*, a tramp

* There is no such thing as an average cigar, as Josephine Babcock protested to the Senate Select Subcommittee on Tobacco Pollution.

steamer fifty miles at sea, he forbade, henceforth and for evermore, the burning of *soja hispida Babcockisis* in the open atmosphere.

When she visited Precious Babykins at his pig farm, Josephine had of course told him of the problem.

'Send some over, Mama,' he said. 'I have my doubts, but maybe the pigs will eat it.'

The pigs would not eat it, no matter what Bubba did with it. Josephine was very disappointed, not so much because the pigs had rejected it, but because it was Bubba's first manifestation of interest in problems affecting Burton Babcock & Company, and it had been a failure.

In desperation, she had turned to one Sydney Prescott, of Sydney Prescott & Associates, Advertising, of New York. The first time Josephine Babcock had seen Ms Prescott, she had loathed her instantly, but business was business. Working on a contingency basis (if the idea worked, she got paid; if it didn't, she didn't), Ms Prescott had upped the sales of Old Billy Goat Snuff, an old-time Burton Babcock & Company product that had about reached the end of the line, beyond credibility. She had not only turned the Old Billy Goat Snuff sales decline around, she had sent it soaring into space with an imaginative campaign that Josephine had to admire, her loathing of Ms Prescott aside.

What Ms Prescott had done was pose one of those bony high-fashion models, the kind who inspire charitable donations for the hungry, in the process of sniffing some Old Billy Goat off the back of her long, bony, lavender-fingernailed hand. There was just one line of advertising copy: 'Up Yours, Sweetie!'

Old Billy Goat, which previously had its market limited essentially to Pennsylvania Dutch farmers, with an even smaller market in the Dakotas, overnight became the 'in' thing of the feminist movement. A tin of Old Billy Goat was even placed beside each plate at the president's wife's Dinner for Outstanding Female Congress-persons, a truly remarkable thing to happen considering that the president's wife knew full well what Josephine had said about her and her husband.

'I'll tell you what, darling,' Ms Prescott said to Mrs Babcock. 'You don't mind if I call you, darling, do you?'

'I most certainly do,' Mrs Babcock replied. 'If you don't wish to replace your dentures, I wouldn't do it again.'

'What I was about to say, Mrs Babcock,' Ms Prescott went on quickly, 'is that Sydney Prescott sees a simple, yet brilliantly imaginative solution to your problem.'

'Which is?'

'Feed *soja hispida Babcockisis* to people,' Ms Prescott said.

'You're as crazy as you look,' Josephine had said, getting right to the bottom line as, she thought of it. 'Precious Babykins . . . I mean to say, my son, Burton Babcock IV, has informed me that even his pigs turn up their snouts at it.'

'Yes, I know,' Ms Prescott replied. 'I had a long chat with Bubba about it.'

'You have spoken with my son?'

'Indeed. And a splendid young chap he certainly is,' Ms Prescott went on. 'They don't grow them like that any more. Six-three, isn't he?'

'Six-four, actually,' Josephine had replied.

'With such sparkling white teeth!'

'I personally supervised Bubba's diet,' Mrs Babcock said. 'Until he went off to College.'

'If you don't mind my saying so, he makes me wish I were twenty years younger.'

'Thirty years would be more like it,' Josephine replied. 'And now that you do mention it, I do mind. You should be ashamed of yourself, at your age!'

'Bubba said that he wasn't surprised that his pigs wouldn't eat it,' Ms Sydney Prescott went on. 'He says that pigs are smarter than people. Well, there you have it!'

'There I have what?'

'We'll call it Wild West Beanos,' Ms Prescott said. 'In anticipation of our meeting, my chief photographer, Lance Fairbanks, and his capable crew are at this very moment scouring the plains of Texas in search of a suitable model for Wild West Beanos. I have the preliminary artwork with me.'

She handed Josephine an artist's sketch of a tin can. There was an 'overline,' an advertising term, designating words that appear above the artwork. This read: '100% Pure – 100% American Grown.'

Then came the words WILD WEST BEANOS in old-West-type letters.

Beneath this was a sketch of a cowboy sitting on his heels before a campfire, holding a skillet presumably containing Wild West Beanos over a wood fire, while his faithful horse watches curiously. The face of the cowboy was blank.

'The cowboy's face is blank,' Josephine observed.

'As I said, Lance Fairbanks is scouring the Texas plains in his Winnebago looking for just the right face, some leathery old cowpoke, you see, to fill in the blank. I hope to have some advance proofs for you within the week.'

Under ordinary circumstances, of course, Mrs Josephine Babcock would have given in, at that point, to the delightful impulse to bodily throw Ms Prescott out of her office. But there was something in Ms Prescott's presentation that precluded that. Precious Babykins was interested in the project! He had actually talked to this creature about it. When you got right down to it, the whole idea could really be said to be Precious Babykins' own idea. He was the one who said that the reason pigs wouldn't eat the goddamned bean was because they were smarter than people. It hadn't taken any genius to proceed from that to the obvious conclusion that since people weren't as smart as pigs, people probably *would* eat *soja hispida Babcockisis*, just so long as it came in the proper package. God knows the corn and wheat growers had them eating stuff she wouldn't feed to the pigs.

'I'll be interested in seeing what you come up with,' Josephine said. 'But don't construe that as any sort of a commitment.

Chapter Four

Unbeknownst to anyone of the Burton Babcock & Company corporate family, their problem with *soja hispida Babcockisis* was one of great interest to America's Most Famous TV Gourmet, Taylor P. Jambon. Indeed, Mr Jambon saw in it a chance to redeem himself, public relations-wise, in the eyes of all the good folks out there in TV Land.

For years, Mr Jambon had had a good thing going with APPLE, of which he had been both the founder and the president. The Association of Pup & Pussy Lovers in Earnest, Inc. had, through the generosity of the American people, not only provided the wherewithal to spay cats at a vast network of cat-spaying establishments which just happened to be owned by Mr Jambon's brother-in-law, but had provided Mr Jambon himself with a very generous tax-exempt expense account on which he could travel the world in great luxury while making appeals for funds for APPLE.

The whole thing had collapsed a year previously when the word had gotten out that Mr Jambon's expense account cost APPLE over thirty-five percent of APPLE's total revenue. The word had also gotten out that Mr Jambon had not, as he led people to believe, been exactly *giving* his time and talent to APPLE, and had, in fact, been drawing an annual advisor's honorarium of seventy-five thousand dollars. And it had become public knowledge that the cat-spaying operation had been charging APPLE precisely three times as much per spay than was the going rate among doctors of veterinary medicine, with the profits reaching Mr Jambon via his brother-in-law.

Mr Jambon was convinced that his whole set of difficulties *vis-à-vis* APPLE was the work of Satan. He could think of no other reason – not even gremlins or little green men from Mars – that could have seen the whole thing collapse literally overnight, and under such circumstances.

He had gone to Vienna, Austria on APPLE business. Americans' Most Beloved Thespian, Patience Throckmorton Worthington, had agreed to do a few television appeals for APPLE, provided only that she be paid twice her usual fee ('Fatso,' she had said to Mr Jambon in her deep, dulcet tone, 'I can't stand bleeping animals. If you expect America's most beloved stage, screen, television and radio personality to make a pitch for you, you can bet your blap it's going to cost. You're going to have to pay Patience through the bleeping nose, if you get my point,') and that the commercials be taped in Vienna, where 'America's Grandmother,' as she was often called, was in hot and lustful (if ultimately futile) pursuit of Boris Alexandrovich Korsky-Rimsakov, the World's Greatest Opera Singer.

Taylor P. Jambon had had no way of knowing, when he arranged for a free flight to Vienna,* that the opera singer whom Patience Throckmorton Worthington was after was an American. (With a name like that, Jambon thought, he should be a Frenchman or a German.) Nor could he have known that the singer's best friends in all the world would turn out to be two butinsky doctors from Spruce Harbor, Maine. Nor that the stars of the most popular television news show, 'One Hour,' Harley Hazardous and Trenchcoat Wally Michaels, would be in Vienna at the same time. Nor that Harley Hazardous and Trenchcoat Wally Michaels and the two doctors

---

* Via the US Air Force's VIP flight detachment; this because Sen. J. Ellwood 'Jaws' Fisch (Radical-Liberal, California), was on the APPLE advisory staff at fifty thousand dollars per annum.

would, of all the saloons in Vienna, choose to booze it up in the same one and become instant pals over several gallons of Old Prague Pale Pilsner. Nor that Harley Hazardous, Trenchcoat Wally Michaels and the two hick doctors shared a mutual loathing of America's Most Beloved Young TV Newsperson, Don Rhotten, who was, as his contribution to APPLE and for only twenty thousand dollars, going to appear with Miss Worthington.

Until the Vienna affair, Mr Jambon had believed that there was sort of a television newspersons' code of honour; that they would not, so to speak, blow the whistle on each other.* It wasn't exactly blowing a whistle, what they did to Don Rhotten, APPLE and Taylor P. Jambon – it was more like sounding an air-raid siren. In addition to running film of 'One Hour' of Mr Jambon, Don Rhotten and Senator Fisch whooping it up with a trio of Viennese dumplings while using APPLE's American Express cards, Hazardous and Michaels had shown film of Patience Throckmorton Worthington taking a quart of straight bourbon aboard the plane to steel herself for the horrifying experience of having to hold a puppy in her lap. There had been a rather detailed report of exactly how the money sent in by the suckers out there in TV Land had been spent, and for the *pièce de résistance* of their shoddy yellow television journalism, they had arranged for the opera singer, Boris Alexandrovich Korsky-Rimsakov, to throw America's Most Beloved Young TV Newsperson, Mr Don Rhotten, into Vienna's famous Volksgarten fountain. The big splash was carried live by satellite into 16,476,000 American homes on the 'ABS Evening News'.**

* He was, obviously, right about this. Harley Hazardous and Trenchcoat Wally Michaels were the exceptions that proved the rule. They had long before been declared *personae non grata* by the other practitioners of the television-news art for other incidents of letting the side down.
** Students of journalism and others interested in public affairs may find a detailed account of all this in a scholarly tome published

43

By the time it was all over and following a little chat with the United States attorney for the southern district of New York, Mr Jambon had decided it was his clear, if painful, duty to disband APPLE and turn over all assets to the American Humane Society. He also had to sign, before witnesses, an agreement in which he henceforth and forevermore would cease and desist raising funds for pups and pussies for any reason whatsoever. The United States attorney had been drunk with power.

'The only reason I'm not taking you to trial, Fatso,' he said, 'is that I would have to put Miss Patience Throckmorton Worthington on trial with you. I just can't find it in my heart to expose that lady for what she is, that is to say, a drunken old alley cat, and destroy the cherished illusions of millions of Americans, including my own wife and children. But if you ever so much as bend over to pet a dog, Jambon, it's slammer time, you understand me?'

Sen. Jaws Fisch, of course, put out a statement that he hardly knew Mr Jambon, and that he could not, of course, know what statements had been made in his name by every one of the 160 members of his staff. Don Rhotten had announced that it was all a misunderstanding, that he himself had been working on what he called the 'exposé of that APPLE mess' and had gone, so to speak, undercover to do so. He denied that he bore Harley Hazardous and Trenchcoat Wally Michaels any ill feeling, and tearfully announced that it was his fondest desire to one day be able to join what he called 'the brave and fearless team of television journalists on "One Hour".'

There had been nothing left for Taylor P. Jambon to

in the public interest by Sphere Books, London. *M*A*S*H Goes to Vienna* is generally to be found on the racks of better-class bookselling establishments from coast to coast at the very reasonable price of a dollar and a half. A fifty percent discount is offered to honest television journalists. (Proof required; applications will be judged by the authors, whose decision will be final.)

do but go about his TV gourmet business with his head held high, and silently reminding himself of the great philosophic truth about 'sticks and stones' and 'the slings and arrows of outrageous fortune'.

There was not, of course, nearly as much money in teaching the nation's housewives how to make Ham Jambon, Oysters Apache, or Tacos Française on the tube as there had been in guiding the affairs of APPLE, and as time (and the terror the United States attorney had instilled) passed, Mr Jambon began to think carefully about what had happened. The consent decree he had signed had only dealt with pups and pussies, canaries and other domestic animals. It had, he realized, had absolutely nothing to say about livestock.

Certainly, he came to believe, there must be money in livestock. Money he could pry loose from the suckers out there in TV Land, the same suckers who had been so generous to the pups and pussies of APPLE.

He toyed with several ideas (among them, a Twilight Years Pasture for worn-out bulls and, what had seemed like pure inspiration, Clothe Our Naked Animal Friends, Inc., only to learn that someone else had thought of it first and threatened instant legal action against him) but nothing, he realized, had the zip, zang and pathos that had made APPLE so successful.

And then he stumbled, more or less, across something that had potential. With the honorarium from APPLE gone, it was necessary for Mr Jambon to hit again what he called 'the cold-chicken and mashed-peas circuit'. He offered himself on the marketplace, in other words, as a speaker. He had three stock speeches written for him by one of Don Rhotten's writers* and gave them, in turn, sometimes all three in one day, while driving around the

* His friendship with Mr Rhotten had continued on a secret basis. Both he and Mr Rhotten were unwilling, no matter what the provocation, to cut off what was for both their only non-business relationship with another human being.

United States. The only thing he asked of his audience was money.

One day, while driving between Fayetteville and Rocky Mount, North Carolina in his mauve-over-tangerine Volvo, en route from one talk to another, a foul odour assailed his nostrils. It was of such overpowering revulsion that it was all Mr Jambon could do to pull off the highway and stop the car.

At first, naturally perhaps, he thought that something was wrong with the car, but when he stopped and turned the engine off, the smell endured. The air conditioner having failed him in his hour of need, the windows open, he came to the logical conclusion that the smell was not the car's fault after all, for the smell was getting worse, not better.

He was, he saw, in a bucolic setting. It reminded him, in fact, of the advertising photographs used to promote Back on the Farm Brand Country Bay-kin and So Sweet Saw-sage, his most loyal sponsor.* There were gently rolling green hills, divided by neat white fences. There was a collection of bright red farm buildings, several silos, and the other to-be-expected accoutrements of a farming situation.

It even, he realized suddenly, smelled like the manufacturing facilities of the Back on the Farm people. Their base of operations was in Hohokus, New Jersey, right across the Hudson River from New York City, and Mr Jambon had been forced by that circumstance to visit the place, even though the smell had made him sick from the moment he got out of the Lincoln Tunnel.

Somewhat surprised that the Back on the Farm folks would have a manufacturing facility so far out here in the boondocks, Mr Jambon put the Volvo in gear and drove to the gate. There was a neatly lettered sign:

---

* Country Bay-kin and So Sweet Saw-sage are made from what the manufacturer terms 'textured proteins'. As a rule of thumb, whenever one reads 'textured proteins', one may presume 'textured soybeans'.

BURTON BABCOCK & COMPANY
POSSIBLE PORCINE PRODUCTS RESEARCH
ESTABLISHMENT
ABSOLUTELY NO ADMITTANCE

'OK, Fatso, the jig's up,' a *very* crude person, armed with a shotgun and dressed in striped overalls and a straw hat, announced.

'My dear chap,' Taylor P. Jambon had replied. 'Do you have any idea whatever whom you are addressing?'

'Just offhand, I'd say it was a fat Yankee hog thief,' the man said. 'Get out of the car, Fatso!' he said, gesturing with the shotgun.

'Whatever for?'

'Cause I'll shoot you if you don't,' the crude person in the overalls had replied, whereupon Mr Jambon had rapidly exited the Volvo. Prodded by the shotgun, America's Most Famous TV Gourmet was led to a small building where a very large, blond young man with a massive chest and pearly white teeth was seated at a desk reading *The Hog Fancier's Journal*.

'Got him, Bubba,' the fellow in the overalls said.

'He looks like a hog thief, all right,' the young man said.

'And he was driving a Volvo, too,' the man with the shotgun added.

'Unfortunately, this fat fellow is not our man, Clarence,' the young man said. 'The sheriff just telephoned from town to report that he apprehended our hog thief in the very act of offering our prizewinning sow, Babcock's Swedish Princess Elfriede XIX, to the Moran Sausage works.'

'Oh, damn!' Clarence said. 'And I was so looking forward to shooting this one!'

'I can understand your feelings,' Bubba replied. 'Tell me, Fat man, who are you and what are you doing here at the Possible Porcine Products Research Establishment?'

'I am Taylor P. Jambon,' he replied, 'America's Most Famous TV Gourmet. That's who I am!'

'And what are you doing here?'

'I was attracted by the smell ' Jambon replied. 'What is that sickening odour, anyway?'

'It's *soja hispida Babcockisis*, actually,' Bubba said.

'I see,' Taylor P. Jambon said.

'It's an experimental hog feed,' Bubba explained.

'You're actually going to feed that foul-smelling concoction to innocent little porkers?' Taylor had exploded.

'We're having a little trouble getting them to eat it, as presently constituted,' Bubba said. 'But, with hard work and some imaginative feeding procedures, yes, that is our ultimate intention.'

'He *is* a trespasser, Bubba,' the chap in the overalls said. 'If I can't shoot him where he stands, how about letting me give him a fifty-yard start and then shooting him?'

'Alas, no, Clarence,' Bubba had replied. 'As desirable an idea as that is to you and me, I'm afraid that Little Mama would disapprove. Just escort him off the premises.'

By the time Taylor P. Jambon was back on the highway, inspiration had struck. Protect Our Precious Porkers, in other words, was born. It was a natural, he knew that in the pit of his stomach. A baby pig is just as appealing as a puppy or kitten. Just as soon as he worked out the details, the money would start rolling in again. In a way, it was better than Pups & Pussies. The end product of a puppy was a dog and the end product of a pussy was a cat. Dogs and cats have to be fed. The reverse was true of a piglet: one ate the final product of a piglet. He'd get the suckers to feed his precious porkers until they reached maturity, and then he'd sell them to the slaughterhouse.

He stopped by the county jail and went bail for the pig thief. He then entered into a business relationship with him. In exchange for his lawyer's fees and a certain amount of money, the pig thief was to keep an eye on the Possible Porcine Products Research Establishment, keeping notes, and taking what photographs he could of how this cruel and inhumane operation was forcing the precious porkers to digest that foul-smelling *soja hispida Babcockisis*. When they had incontrovertible proof of this, Taylor P. Jambon would get his pal Don Rhotten to break the story, giving him full credit, naturally, on the 'ABS Evening News'.

Taylor P. Jambon had been so excited by this new turn of events that he cancelled the rest of his speaking engagements and returned directly to his Beverly Hills home.

Two weeks later, the pig thief had telephoned with bad news. The pig feeding had failed; the pigs would not eat the *soja hispida Babcockisis* no matter how the people at the Possible Porcine Products Research Establishment had tried to disguise the taste.

It was, of course, a crushing disappointment. It meant going back on the road and giving talks to all those blue-haired rural women.

'Rome, my pig-stealing friend,' Taylor P. Jambon had replied, 'wasn't built in a day. You keep your eye on that place and those people. Sooner or later, that broad-chested chap with the pearly teeth is going to do something beastly to my precious porkers, or my name isn't Taylor P. Jambon.'

Chapter Five

A week later, a UPS messenger delivered an enormous package of eleven-by-fourteen-inch black-and-white and full-colour photographs to the executive suite of Burton Babcock & Company.

They showed a battered old cowboy of the west Texas plains and his faithful Indian companion. Unlike the preliminary artwork, which showed the cowboy at a camp-fire, the photographs depicted the cowboy and the Indian on the crude and falling-down porch of an ancient, falling-down ranch house. There was even a buffalo, one visibly past his prime, who stood eyeing the camera suspiciously.

How this trio was going to entice the American consumer into buying, much less eating, a bean the pigs wouldn't eat was frankly beyond Josephine Babcock's understanding. But neither – she told herself as she examined the leathery face, the somewhat-bloodshot blue eyes, and dirty grey hair of the old cowboy – had she been able to understand how Sydney Prescott had been able to get millions of women to start sniffing snuff, as she had with Old Billy Goat. (Old Billy Goat, now Olde Billie Goat, continued to expand its sales, and was closing in, sales-wise, on Mountain Lion Plug Cut Chewing Tobacco, dollar-wise.)

'Ernestine,' Josephine Babcock said to her senior executive secretary, 'have them bring a car around. I'm going to the pig parlour.'

'One of the Rolls, Mrs Babcock?' Ernestine replied,

'It's a nice day; you could put the roof down on the Corniche.'

'No, I think not. I'm going to the farm. I'll rough it. Have them bring the Cadillac pick-up around.* I'll even drive it myself.'

An hour later, Mrs Babcock came upon her son. Dressed only in a pair of khaki trousers converted to shorts, a pair of aviator-type sunglasses, and a broad-brimmed straw hat, Precious Babykins was guiding a 250-horsepower Burton 'Green Giant' diesel tractor through the fields. The sun caused his pearly white teeth to glisten rather attractively against the tanned darkness of his skin. His massive chest was moist with honest sweat.

Precious Babykins, his mother decided, was proof positive of how well she had done her maternal duty to the poor, fatherless boy. And her duty on earth was nearly over. All she had to do now was (a) get him off the damned tractor and into the executive suite and (b) see him march down the aisle on the arm of some suitable female.

'Hello, there, Little Mama,' Precious Babykins said in his deep, masculine voice, after he had jumped nimbly from the Green Giant diesel tractor. 'What brings you out here?'

'Too much sun isn't good for you, Pre . . . Bubba,' Josephine said.

'You didn't come all the way out here to tell me that, did you, Little Mama?'

'I came to show you these, Bubba,' she said, handing him the enormous envelope. 'This is how that horrid Sydney Prescott woman thinks we can get rid of the *soja hispida Babcockisis*.'

'Huh!' he said. It was sort of a snort, and she didn't quite know what he meant by it.

He examined the photos.

* Those who question the existence of Cadillac pick-up trucks are referred to spring-summer, 1976, catalogue of Neiman-Marcus Company, Dallas, Texas.

'I'll be damned,' he said. 'This may solve our problem completely!'

'You really think so, dear?' she replied. 'And watch your language!'

'Forgive me, Little Mama,' he said. 'No offence intended.'

'I forgive you, Precious Babykins,' she said, and pinched his cheek.

'Do you know where these photographs were taken?'

'Somewhere in Texas,' she said.

'I'm going right out there,' Bubba said.

'Bubba,' Josephine said, 'you must try to remember that you're a Babcock. You don't *go* to see people. You *send* for people, and they come to you.'

'Mother,' he said, 'by your own statement, we don't have any solution for *soja hispida Babcockisis*. We can't get people to smoke it any more, the pigs won't eat it, and we can't even burn it, by presidential executive order. This is no time to stand on protocol!'

'You're right, Precious Babykins!' she said.

'Mother, I've asked you, and I've asked you. Please don't call me that!'

'Bubba, it just slips out!' she said.

'Well, knock it off!' he said, angrily, sounding just like his late daddy when he was piqued. He turned back to the Green Giant tractor and picked up the CB microphone.

'Breaker, breaker,' he said, 'this is the Old Pigman. You got your ears on, Bald Eagle?'

'Come back, Pigman,' the radio crackled. 'You got the Old Bald Eagle.'

'Warm up the bird, Bald Eagle. Pigman's leaving his work Ten-Twenty for the Bird Nest at this time. Come back.'

'Ten-four, Pigman. Where're we going? Come back.'

'Don't know yet, Bald Eagle. I've got to get that Ten-twenty from Little Mama. Some place in Texas. Come back.'

52

'Ten-four, Pigman, the Old Bald Eagle's going Ten-ten and standing by.'

'Ten-four, Bald Eagle. This is the Old Pigman, King King Queen Seven Zero One Zero, Mobile Unit Four, we're down and gone.'

'Am I correct in inferring, Bubba, that that was Colonel Merritt T. Charles, US Army, retired, the pilot of your personal Learjet, with whom you were speaking?' Josephine asked.

'That's right, Little Mama,' Bubba replied. 'We're going to head for Texas. What I want you to do is find out where the photographs were taken, and get that information to me while we're en route.'

'Of course, dear,' she said. 'I'll get right through to that terrible woman on the telephone and find out.'

'You can drop me at the airport,' Bubba said, getting behind the wheel of the Cadillac pick-up truck. 'I really hate to leave this field half-ploughed, but these are special circumstances.'

'I understand completely, dear,' Josephine said. 'And I must tell you that I am touched at this display of interest in the corporate problems of Burton Babcock & Company.'

'As you yourself are always saying, Little Mama,' Bubba said, as he put his foot to the floor, causing the Cadillac pick-up to rocket away from the field, 'what's good for Burton Babcock & Company is good for the country.'

Josephine Babcock, a little tear in her eye, reached for the microphone dangling from the CB in the cab of the Cadillac pick-up.

'Breaker, breaker,' she said. 'Typewriter Lady, you got your ears on? This is Little Mama. Come back.'

'You got Typewriter Lady,' the radio replied. 'Come back, Little Mama.'

'Typewriter Lady, get Weird Beaver on a landline and find out where those photographs were taken. Precious . . . Old Pigman's on his way out there.'

53

'Ten-four, Little Mama,' Typewriter Lady (who was, of course, Mrs Babcock's senior executive secretary), replied. 'Stand by.'

'Bubba, darling,' Josephine said, 'please don't take offence. But aren't you dressed, well, a little *informally*, shall I say, to be going all the way to Texas?'

'I always keep a tee shirt, a pair of jeans and a pair of jump boots in the plane, Little Mama,' Bubba replied. 'Against just such an unforeseen contingency as this.'

'You're planning to parachute into Texas?'

'There's no better way to go, Little Mama,' Bubba said. 'I've told you that.'

And so, fifteen minutes later, she had watched her first- (and only) born soar off from Babcock Airfield (also known as the Bird Nest) in his personal Learjet. While she would really have preferred that he land in the airplane rather than jump out of it, on balance, she was delighted. Bubba was finally showing an interest in corporate affairs. Once he had nibbled at the fruit, she was convinced, he would be hooked. She would have him in a white shirt and tie and highly polished shoes in no time at all.

Four days later, the little blue light on Josephine Babcock's very personal telephone began to glow. Only eight people, among them Precious Babykins knew that number, and even as she reached to pick up the phone, some maternal extrasensory perception told her that it would, indeed, be Precious Babykins.

'Hello darling,' she said. 'I've missed you so much!'

'This is Colonel Charles, ma'am,' the Old Bald Eagle said, rather embarrassed. 'Mr Burton Babcock IV is calling.' Then, she heard him say, 'Bubba, I've got your mother,' and then Bubba came on the line.

'Mother?' he said.

'Yes, dear? How did things go in Texas?'

'I can't tell you how well, Mother,' Bubba said. 'You'll have to see for yourself. Can you meet me at the airfield?'

'Of course, I can, darling,' she said.

'We'll be there in thirty minutes,' Bubba said. 'Mother, I must tell you that I really didn't believe you. But it happened!'

'Believe me about what? What happened?'

'I'll explain all at the airfield,' Bubba said. 'I'm sure you'll be as happy as I am, Mother, dear,' Bubba said. 'Until then, Little Mama!'

Twenty-nine minutes and thirty seconds later, as Josephine Babcock waited at Babcock Airfield in the yellow Rolls Corniche, practically beside herself with mingled feminine and maternal curiosity, Burton Babcock & Company Learjet Number Three, Bubba's personal airplane, zoomed across the field at no more than fifty feet, did a barrel roll, and then climbed to about five thousand feet where it levelled out.

She didn't want to look, for she knew what was about to happen, but she had to. A little black speck, which she knew with a sinking feeling in her stomach was Precious Babykins, detached itself from the Learjet and fell like a rock towards earth.

She held her breath (eventually she turned a little blue) until Bubba pulled the D ring on the rip cord and the parachute canopy filled with air. It opened at no more than five hundred feet off the earth, close enough for her to be able to see Precious Babykins' pearly white teeth exposed in the happiest smile she could ever recall.

He landed five feet away from her with a little bounce and, as soon as he had collapsed the canopy and gotten out of the harness, he bounded over to her and gave her a hug and a kiss.

'I'm so ashamed that I didn't believe you, Little Mama,' he said. 'But I didn't.'

'Believe me about what, Precious Babykins?'

'I'm so happy, Little Mama, that I'll overlook you calling me that,' Bubba said. 'About the heavenly music, that's what.'

'Bubba, darling, what the hell are you talking about?'

she had asked.

'That, Little Mama!' Bubba replied, gesturing towards the sky. Josephine followed his gesture. A second parachutist was in the sky, floating earthward beneath an already-opened parachute canopy.

'I told her to pop it at twenty-five hundred feet,' he said. 'That's only her third free fall, you see.'

'Bubba, darling,' Josephine said, 'are your mother's old ears failing her or did you say *her*?'

'I said *her*, Little Mama,' Bubba said. 'Can't you tell, already, although she is still, I would judge, about one thousand feet up there, how wonderful she is?'

From one thousand feet, all Josephine could see was that whomever her was, her had long blonde hair and had been generously endowed, anatomically speaking, in the bosom department.

'Someone you met in Texas, I gather?' Josephine, forcing herself to smile, said.

'Isn't she wonderful?' Bubba said. 'We wanted you to be the first to know, of course.'

'The first to know what?' she asked, with ten pounds of lead in her stomach.

Bubba didn't reply. The generously endowed blonde parachutist was about to touch down, and he ran over to the touchdown site. Shamelessly, Josephine thought, he embraced the other parachutist the moment she was on the ground, kissed her, and then with his arm around her, marched her over to where Josephine stood leaning (she felt a little woozy) against the Rolls-Royce Corniche.

'Mother, this is Scarlett,' Bubba said. 'Scarlett, this is my mother.'

'Hello, Mrs Babcock,' the blonde said. 'Whatever must you think of me for dropping in on you this way?'

'How do you do?' Josephine Babcock said, rather icily. 'I'm always happy to meet one of Precious Babykins' little playmates.'

'I knew you'd hit it off together right from the start,' Bubba said, with one of them under each arm.

'I didn't quite get the last name,' Josephine said.

'Jones,' Bubba replied. 'Scarlett Rose-Marie Jones. Isn't that a lovely name?'

'Delightful,' Josephine said. Her brain churning furiously now, Josephine remembered reading somewhere that the worst way to rid one's offspring of undesirable associates, in particular those of the opposite gender, was to let your disapproval show. No matter how painful it would be, she vowed, she would not make that error.

'Welcome to Burton County, Miss Jones,' Josephine said, with an ear-to-ear smile. 'I'm so glad to see you.'

'Thank you,' Scarlett said. 'Bubba's told me so much about you. How you've been both mother and father to him.'

'I was just doing my duty,' Josephine said.

'Scarlett and I are going to be married, Mother,' Bubba announced. 'Just as soon as possible!'

'How nice!' Josephine said. 'I've always regarded marriage highly.'

This big-boobed blonde was not, Josephine vowed passionately if silently, going to snatch Precious Babykins from his mother's arms. But how to stop it?

'You must tell me all about yourself, Miss Jones,' Josephine said. 'Who, for example, are your parents and what does your father do?'

'Scarlett lives with her uncle, Mother,' Bubba replied quickly, answering for Scarlett. He really hated not being able to tell Little Mama the truth, the whole truth and nothing but the truth, but the cold fact was that Scarlett's father was a United States congressman (the Honourable 'Alamo' Jones, D., Texas) and Bubba knew that if this came out before he and Scarlett were firmly knotted together in the bonds of matrimony, Little Mama would do whatever she considered necessary to keep the knot from being tied. She would put up with practically anything, Bubba knew, but being related, even by marriage, to a congressman was too much to ask.

'Oh, I see,' Josephine replied.

'My Uncle Hiram,' Scarlett replied. 'Actually my granduncle.'

'I see,' Josephine repeated.

'Uncle Hiram –' Bubba said, 'he has given me permission to call him Uncle Hiram – Mama, holds the key to our little *soja hispida Babcockisis* problem.'

'He does?' Josephine asked, brightening visibly.

'He's a buffalo rancher,' Scarlett said.

'He's a what?'

'*Bison Americanus*,' Bubba clarified. 'Sometimes called *bison bison*. Of the family *Bovidae*.'

'You know, Mother Babcock,' Scarlett said, 'like on those old-time nickels.'

'*What* did you call me?' Josephine asked, visibly shocked.

'She called you Mother Babcock,' Bubba said. 'Isn't that sweet?'

'Yes, it is,' Josephine replied, without much evident enthusiasm. *Mother Babcock, indeed!* she thought. 'And how does Uncle Hiram's buffalo ranch tie in with the bean, darling?'

'They love it,' Bubba said. 'I took two one-hundred-pound sacks of dehydrated *soja hispida Babcockisis* with me when I went to Texas. Say what you like about Ms Sydney Prescott, Mama, she was right on the ball with her buffalo idea.'

'In the excitement of the moment, dear,' Josephine said, 'I'm afraid your old mother's head is a little confused. What exactly does Ms Prescott have to do with Uncle Hiram and his buffaloes?'

'Why, she sent those photographs back from Texas, Mother,' Bubba replied, obviously surprised that his mother had so quickly forgotten. 'The ones that sent me winging my way to Texas and into Scarlett's heart!'

This declaration of love triggered a like emotion in Scarlett Rose-Marie Jones. She reached up and nuzzled Bubba in the neck. Josephine shuddered.

'The photographs that woman sent were of some broken-down whisky-soaked old bum of a cowboy,' Josephine said. 'And an equally drunken and broken-down old Indian.'

'Mother Babcock,' Scarlett Rose-Marie Jones said, icily, 'I hope, of course, that our relationship will be a warm one, but I must insist that you never again refer to my Uncle Hiram and Sitting Buffalo, his faithful Indian companion, in those terms.'

'I'm sure Little Mama meant no harm, precious,' Bubba said. 'Did you, Mother?'

'Of course not,' Josephine said. 'I was just making a little joke.'

'You've got a weird sense of humour, Mother Babcock,' Scarlett said. 'I'll say that.'

'As I was saying, Mother, I had some dehydrated *soja hispida Babcockisis* with me, and when I mixed it with water, Teddy Roosevelt gobbled it up.'

'Teddy Roosevelt?'

'He's Uncle Hiram's pet buffalo,' Scarlett explained.

'Of course,' Josephine said.

'And Hawkeye said, when I showed him the chemical analysis . . .'

'Hawkeye is that handsome Indian in the photographs of your charming uncle?' Josephine asked.

'No,' Bubba said. 'Hawkeye is a doctor. Of medicine. I mean, not a buffalo doctor, actually, but someone with training in the field of nutrition.'

'Of course,' Josephine said.

'We met him at the Saints-Cowboys game,' Bubba explained.*

'The Indian in the photograph is Sitting Buffalo,' Scarlett clarified.

'As I was saying,' Bubba went on, 'Hawkeye said,

* Those with a burning desire to know the circumstances under which Hawkeye and Trapper John happened to be so far from the rockbound coast of Maine are referred to *M*A*S*H Goes to Texas* (Sphere Books, London) in which the facts have been laid bare without fear or favour.

and Trapper John agreed . . .'

'Trapper John?'

'He's a doctor, too,' Scarlett said.

'That there was something in the digestive system, probably a very strong gastric acid of some kind, that permits the *bison Americanus*' digestive tract to handle *soja hispida Babcockis*. Just as soon as I make some preliminary arrangements for our wedding, I'm going to have Old Bald Eagle fly a couple of tons of dehydrated *soja hispida Babcockisis* out there, and to bring a dozen of the beasts back here to the pig ranch.'

'What a brilliant idea!' Josephine said. 'But wouldn't it perhaps be better, dear, if I might make a little suggestion, to postpone your nuptials until after we see what the bean does to the buffaloes over, say, a ninety-day period?'

'I asked Hawkeye for his wise, physician's opinion of my burning desire to take Scarlett as my bride as soon as possible,' Bubba said.

'Why would you ask him? I mean, who is this man? Wouldn't it make more sense to ask your own mother?'

'Hawkeye is an FFF, Mother,' Bubba said.

'And so is Trapper John, Mother Babcock,' Scarlett said.

'An FFF, as in Framingham Theosophical Foundation Fellow? That kind of FFF?'

'Yes, indeed,' Bubba said. 'FTFF, just like dear Dad, may he rest in peace.'

'How do you know this?'

'Hawkeye and Trapper John, of course, are far too modest to boast about something like that, of course,' Bubba said.

'Rev. Mother Emeritus told us,' Scarlett said.

'Rev. Mother Emeritus?'

'While we were waiting for Uncle Hiram and Mr Horsey to be released from ja . . .' Scarlett said and stopped.

'Released from where?' Josephine said, pouncing on Scarlett.

'A gross miscarriage of justice, Mama,' Bubba said. 'Growing out of a simple misunderstanding.'

'I see,' Josephine said. 'And who is Mr Horsey? Another Indian?'

'He's a cajun, actually,' Scarlett said. 'And it's really *Colonel* de la Chevaux.'

'Tell me more about the Reverend Mother Emeritus and the two FFF doctors,' Josephine said. 'You didn't happen to learn their real names, did you?'

'Benjamin Franklin Pierce, MD, FACS, FFF,' Bubba said. 'That's Hawkeye.'

'And John Francis Xavier McIntyre, MD, FACS, FFF,' Scarlett added.

'And what did these Framingham Fellows have to say when you asked them about your burning desire to rush into marriage?' Josephine asked.

'Hawkeye said it was better to marry than to burn,' Scarlett said, and blushed.

'And Trapper John said that love was what makes the world go 'round,' Bubba said.

'And the Reverend Mother Emeritus?'

'She offered to perform the ceremony herself right then and there,' Bubba said. 'The governor was there, too, you see, to get Uncle Hiram and Mr Horsey out of the slammer, and he was willing to waive the three-day waiting period.

'But Little Mama,' Bubba went on, 'Scarlett said that, being a woman, too, she understood how important it would be for you to be at the wedding of your only son, and that we should wait until you have met one another.'

'How right you were, Miss Jones,' Josephine said. 'Well, children, I suggest we go to the Cottage. You can freshen up, dear Miss Jones, and I have a telephone call or two to make.'

'I put it to you, Mr Framingham,' Josephine Babcock said to Matthew Q. Framingham VI over long-distance telephone, 'not only as a mother determined to save her son from the clutches of a long-haired blonde gold digger, but as the widow of a Framingham Foundation Fellow, my late beloved husband, may he rest in peace, that your foundation generally, and these two doctors specifically, have a moral obligation to stop this ill-advised marriage.'

'My dear Mrs Babcock,' Matthew Q. Framingham replied. 'I am astounded to hear that Dr Pierce and Dr McIntyre have actually encouraged these two misguided young people to enter the state of matrimony. I know from my own personal experience that both are as opposed to marriage as I am myself.'

'You are not suggesting that my Precious Babykins lied to his Little Mama, are you, Framingham?' Mrs Babcock said, in a menacing snarl.

'Perish the thought, dear lady,' Matthew replied. 'I merely meant to suggest the possibility that your son misunderstood Dr Pierce and/or Dr McIntyre.'

'Watch it!' she said.

'Dear lady,' Matthew said, 'just as soon as I finish speaking with you, I will personally communicate with the fellows in question, and do my level best to ascertain the facts in this situation.'

'It's the least you can do,' she said. 'For the widow of an FFF.'

'I was about to say precisely that,' Matthew said.

'Especially one who authorizes the annual Burton Babcock & Company Burton Babcock III Memorial Bequest to the Framingham Foundation.'

'You could put it that way, I suppose.'

'That's the way I do put it, Mr Framingham,' Josephine said. 'I will be awaiting your call. Get back to me at your convenience, any time within the next hour or so.'

Chapter Six

Through what Wallington T. Dowd, the head Texas Ranger, called 'a lamentable little misunderstanding', Mrs Ida-Sue Jones, wife to the Honourable 'Alamo' Jones, member of Congress, and mother of Scarlett, had been arrested and incarcerated by two Texas Rangers.

For reasons that are better not delved into deeply, the Texas Rangers who put the cuffs on Ida-Sue and threw her in the slammer were under the impression that she was the 'white female, age unknown, described as quote the sort of cheap blonde hussy who would trifle with a poor old man's affection unquote' whom a priority, all-points bulletin from Texas Rangers Headquarters had ordered them to find and jug.

Ironically, the all-points bulletin had been issued at Ida-Sue's request. She had been concerned, for reasons having nothing whatever to do with familial love, with the location of her husband's paternal uncle, one Hiram Jones, of the T Bar X Ranch, near Midland, Texas. Mr Jones had last been seen in his pick-up truck, headed in the general direction of Dallas, Texas, and in the company of a 'good-looking, large-busted blonde'.*

Ida-Sue Jones was looking for her paternal uncle-by-marriage for what she considered good and valid cause. 'The Old Bum,' as she spoke privately of him, was obviously bereft of his senses. He had lived for thirty years in a run-down and ramshackle old cabin on the old T Bar X, his sole companions an Indian chap with a legend-

---

* The lady in question was actually Scarlett Rose-Marie Jones, but Ida-Sue Jones had no way of knowing this at the time.

ary fondness for the bottle and a herd of buffalo including one large, somewhat weather-beaten old bull whom he called Teddy Roosevelt, and whom he led around, wherever he went, on a leash like a dog.

Under ordinary circumstances, Ida-Sue would have been perfectly happy to leave Uncle Hiram in peace on the old T Bar X, indeed to hope that he never left the premises. One who aspires to be First Lady of this great land of ours, to set up housekeeping at government expense at 1600 Pennsylvania Avenue in our nation's capital, can well do without a family member who is a smelly old bum with a buffalo bull on a leash. That sort of thing tends to detract from the image one is trying to project.

But something had come up. In an attempt to secure the friendship, and thus the considerable influence, on Capitol Hill and elsewhere of the Honourable Vladimir T. 'Vibrato Val' Vishnefsky (Polish-Republican, Illinois) and the Honourable Antonio J. 'Tiny Tony' Bambino (Ethnic-Democrat, New Jersey) for her husband, Alamo Dave, Ida-Sue had decided to see that each of these distinguished members of Congress had an oil well of their very own.

Ida-Sue had some time before come to understand that how one feels toward the oil industry frequently depends on whether or not one owns an oil well. Thus, she reasoned, if Vibrato Val and Tiny Tony each came into an oil well, it would not be too much to hope that they would stop saying all those rude things about Alamo Dave and, in time, join the so-far, frankly, rather thin ranks of those who wanted to see Alamo Dave in the White House.

Vibrato Val and Tiny Tony were interested in her little proposition, and both drew cheques on the Congressional Stationery Allowance Account to make the investment. Now, every time one 'sinks a hole' (as drilling an oil well is known to the cognoscenti), one does not find oil. Vibrato Val and Tiny Tony were not aware of this little technicality and they, having invested their hard-earned stationery allowances, expected to get an oil well with oil in it in return.

Ida-Sue, not knowing this, had early on decided not to even bother sinking holes for her husband's distinguished colleagues from Congress. She would simply send them a cheque and tell them she had sunk holes and that the holes had come in gushers. And she did this.

At this point, the difficulty began. No sooner had Vibrato Val and Tiny Tony cashed their first cheques and had a word with the Speaker of the House *vis-à-vis* getting themselves assigned to the House Committee on Oil Industry Regulation that they announced they wanted to see their oil wells in person.

'Once you've seen óne oil well, Congressmen,' Ida-Sue had tried to reason with them, 'you've seen them all. You can save yourself a long and expensive trip by simply watching the Exxon commercials on TV.'

'Not to worry, little lady,' Vibrato Val said. 'Travel is broadening, as I always say.'

'And don't worry about the expenses, *cara mia*,' Tiny Tony had chimed in. 'We'll have the air force fly us down there.'

All of this had taken place at a very bad time for Ida-Sue, personally. She was having trouble with Scarlett Rose-Marie. Ida-Sue, while at the University of Texas, had been a University of Texas Marching Band Pompon Girl. Indeed, she had been doing a 'Texas, Texas, rah-rah-rah' when she had first seen Alamo Dave. Even with her head stuck between her legs so that Alamo Dave, then a second-string halfback, had been upside down, it had been lust at first sight.

From the moment Scarlett Rose-Marie was born, nine months and three weeks later, Ida-Sue had yearned eagerly for the day when little Scarlett herself would be a UTMBPG and Ida-Sue would become eligible for membership in Texas' most exclusive social organization for women, the University of Texas Marching Band

Pompon Girls' Mommies. Such membership was limited to former UTMBPG's whose daughters were also UTMBPG's.

When Vibrato Val and Tiny Tony had called to announce they were Texas bound to see their oil wells, Ida-Sue had been in Houston, at the Shamrock Hotel, for the annual Bar-B-Que Banquet and *thé danse* of the Association of Former UTMBPG's.*

Ida-Sue had, over the twenty years since Scarlett Rose-Marie had first seen the light of day, given much thought to the happy days when she would become a UTMBPG's Mommy, and she had gone to the Shamrock Hotel with what she considered a splendid plan:

Instead of just standing up when her name, and Scarlett's, were called by Madame Chairperson at the UTMBPG Bar-B-Que Banquet, she would do a cheer just to show the others that the trials and tribulations of marriage, motherhood and striving for the highest wifely office in the land had not prematurely aged her.

She had the routine all worked out. Scarlett would do the pompon waving for the 'Texas, Texas' and Ida-Sue would come in on the 'rah-rah-rah', ending her bit with the split that had so often caused the stands to explode with applause in her day.

Scarlett, however, when Ida-Sue got to the Shamrock Hotel, was difficult about the whole thing.

'Mother,' she said, 'there has to be more to life than bouncing up and down in front of a horde of leering men!'

'Bite your tongue!' Ida-Sue snapped.

'Well, you can make a fool of yourself if you want,' the ungrateful child had said. 'But count me out.'

'What do you mean, "count me out"?' Ida-Sue demanded.

'You'd find out soon enough anyway, Mother,'

---

* The UTMBPG Mommies was an elite organization within the larger organization, similar to the Shrine within the Masonic order, and the Order of the Cootie within the VFW.

66

Scarlett said. 'You might as well hear it from me. I've turned in my pompons. Never again!'

'You can't mean it?'

'I mean it,' Scarlett had gone on. 'And I'm leaving school. I don't know where or what I'll be doing, but with a little bit of luck, maybe I'll find something important to do with my life.'

'You've just stuck a dagger into your mother's heart,' Ida-Sue replied.

At that very moment, the call had come from Congressmen Vishnefsky and Bambino. When Ida-Sue had finally hung up, Scarlett Rose-Marie had vanished. Vowing that she would never forgive her daughter for humiliating her in this fashion, Ida-Sue turned her attention to the problem of producing an oil well, a flowing oil well, from, so to speak, thin air.

It was at that point that she remembered crazy old Uncle Hiram.

Crazy old Uncle Hiram was really Hiram Jones, Jr., eldest son of his father. As such he had inherited fifty-one percent of the old T Bar X Ranch, forty-nine percent having gone to Alamo's father, the late Bosworth T. Jones. Even when oil had been discovered under the forty-nine percent of the old T Bar X, which had come into Alamo's possession, Uncle Hiram had refused to drill for it on his own fifty-one percent.

'I don't want those noisy, dirty derricks scaring my buffalo,' he had announced. 'And I have all the money I need. *I'm* not trying to buy my wife the White House.'

Alamo had then suggested that they have The Old Bum locked up in a padded cell, but Ida-Sue had counselled patience.

'Look at it this way, Stupid,' she had said to her husband. 'The Old Bum won't live forever. You're his only living blood relative . . .'

'Scarlett is a living blood relative,' Alamo Jones had corrected her.

'I've told you and told you, Dummy,' Ida-Sue had

replied. 'Don't correct me.'

'Sorry, Ida-Sue,' he had said.

'As I was saying, Stupid,' Ida-Sue went on, 'The Old Bum is going to kick off soon enough, leaving you as his only blood relative. That means you get the ranch anyway. We can wait. It's better than having the news that you've got an uncle in the funny farm come out in the middle of an election campaign.'

'This is an observation, Ida-Sue,' Alamo said, carefully. 'Not a correction.'

'What is?'

'What if Uncle Hiram should get married? Or leave a will bequeathing his estate to Sitting Buffalo, his faithful Indian companion?'

'Who would marry that dirty old man?' Ida-Sue responded. 'And this is Texas, not Massachusetts. Texans don't leave things to Indians, faithful companions or not.'

'Whatever you say, Ida-Sue,' Alamo had replied.

'That's what I keep telling you, Stupid,' Ida-Sue said.

Ida-Sue recalled this incident at the Shamrock Hotel, when faced with the prospect of producing a flowing oil well for Congressmen Vishnefsky and Bambino. There was oil under Uncle Hiram's fifty-one percent of the old T Bar X Ranch. They knew that, for other people's oil-drilling rigs were built right up to the barbed fence.

Far better, Ida-Sue had reasoned, to have it come out that one had a relative who required treatment for a nervous condition than to have Vibrato Val and Tiny Tony piqued for having been hoodwinked. It was as simple as that: the time had come for The Old Bum to be carried off to the funny farm.

Enlisting the services of Andrew Jackson 'Fat Jack' Stewing, MD, fellow, American Society of Practising Psychiatrists, and Richard 'Dirty Dick' Crochet, LLD, attorney and counsellor-at-law, Ida-Sue had gone out to the old T Bar X bent on bundling poor Uncle Hiram up in a straitjacket only to learn that The Old Bum had taken off in his pick-up accompanied by his faithful Indian companion, a large-bosomed blonde, and Teddy Roosevelt.*

Cleverly appealing to head Texas Ranger Wallington T. Dowd's dedication to sweeping the streets of Texas clean of loonies,** Ida-Sue arranged for an all-points bulletin to be issued by the Texas Rangers calling for the arrest and detention of Uncle Hiram, the Indian (whose name was Sitting Buffalo), the blonde hussy last seen with Uncle Hiram, and Teddy Roosevelt.

In a gross miscarriage of justice, two Rangers arrested Ida-Sue in the belief that she was the blonde hussy, and four more arrested Congressmen Vishnefsky and Bambino in the belief that they were Uncle Hiram and Teddy Roosevelt.

It took a little time to have everyone concerned released from their unjust confinement. Normally, all it would have taken would have been for Alamo Jones to call the governor and secure from him, as a professional courtesy between politicians, gubernatorial pardons, at the request of His Excellency, the governor of Louisiana, to his wife, to the two senators, to Col. Jean-Pierre de la Chevaux (Louisiana National Guard, retired), who had also been arrested by mistake, and, at the request of the secretary of state, to his Royal Highness Sheikh Abdullah ben Abzug, who had been arrested with Colonel de la Chevaux.

By the time the governor got around to ordering Ida-Sue's release, her natural pique at being unjustly detained had resulted in a battery of other charges, ranging from 'the use of foul and abusive language to a Texas

---

* She acquired this information from the proprietor of the Lone Star Saloon & Gas Station near the old T Bar X. This luminary simply presumed that Hiram's niece-by-marriage would know Hiram's pet buffalo by name. He erred.

** She announced the endowment of the Wallington T. Dowd Memorial Scholarship for Law Enforcement Studies at Ranger Dowd's alma mater, the Southwest Texas Cattle & Law Man College at Snake Rock.

Ranger in the execution of his official duties' through 'drunk and disorderly conduct' (in this case, requiring Ida-Sue to take the prescribed shower), and it was twenty-four hours before the cell door finally swung open for her.

By hiring the entire Texas force of Super Sleuth Private Detective & Anti-Cattle Rustling Security Services, Inc., Ida-Sue was able to piece together some very disturbing facts, about both Uncle Hiram and about her daughter.

Uncle Hiram had apparently really gone off the deep end. It was known that he had left Texas, taking his pet buffalo and Sitting Buffalo, his faithful Indian companion with him, in the company of a person identified as the Reverend Mother Emeritus Margaret, of the God Is Love in All Forms Christian Church, Inc. It was believed, but not confirmed, that Uncle Hiram was in love with this person and had proposed marriage.*

Super Sleuth Private Detective & Anti-Cattle Rustling Security Services, Inc. reported they had nothing to report *vis-à-vis* Teddy Roosevelt, but they were working on the matter, diligently pursuing several hot clues, and hoped to have information for Ida-Sue shortly.

Super Sleuth reported that a female subject answering the description of Scarlett Rose-Marie Jones (that is to say, a big-breasted blonde) had been seen at the Greater Dallas Sky Diving Association, taking basic parachuting instruction from an individual she was heard referring to as 'Bubba Darling', and who was believed to be a Green Beret HALO technician in civilian clothing. Both were believed to have left Texas, having hitchhiked aboard a Learjet belonging to Burton Babcock & Company, which had landed at the Greater Dallas Sky Diving Association Airfield for fuel. Their destination was unknown.

---

* This report was in error. Uncle Hiram had fallen in love at first sight with Esther Flanagan, RN, of Spruce Harbor, Maine. Rev. Mother Emeritus had only, as she put it, 'agreed to act as Cupid's helper' in the romance.

'My God, Stupid,' Ida-Sue Jones had cried out to her husband in their suite at the Dallas Holiday Inn, 'do you realize what this means?'

'Of course, I do darling,' Alamo Jones had replied. 'Our little Scarlett has finally found a fella.'

'What it means, Lamebrain,' Ida-Sue said, 'is that our carefully laid plans to lead this country out of the shadows of night and into the bright sunshine of the future under your presidential administration have been derailed.'

'I don't quite follow you, Ida-Sue,' Alamo Jones confessed.

'How many votes do you think you're going to get in the Northeast if they find out your only daughter is married to a warmonger? Why couldn't she have fallen for a deserter or hippie? That would have put Massachusetts in your pocket.'

'I see your point,' Alamo Jones said. 'I'll have a little talk with the secretary of the army and get him to tell this fella to leave our little Scarlett alone.'

'And Uncle Hiram!' Ida-Sue went on. 'If we're to believe Super Sleuth, this horrible woman, this gold digger, is going to go back on her vows of poverty, chastity and obedience, and leave the Church and marry Uncle Hiram.'

'That's really shocking!' Alamo Jones said.

'Don't be too hard on her, Stupid,' Ida-Sue said. 'I'd do the same thing myself, under the circumstances. It isn't every day a girl gets a chance to marry a hundred-million-barrel proven oil reserve. Ordinarily, I'd be cheering her on, but this is my hundred-million-barrel proven oil reserve she's marrying, and that's going too far.'

'I see your point,' Alamo said. 'What are we going to do, darling?'

'Shut up and let me think,' Ida-Sue snapped.

As this conversation was taking place, one of the ladies in question, Rev. Mother Emeritus Margaret with Uncle Hiram, Sitting Buffalo, Teddy Roosevelt and Col.

Jean-Pierre de la Chevaux in tow arrived in New Orleans, Louisiana.

A glistening black Cadillac limousine and a swamp buggy were waiting at the Chevaux Petroleum hangar, the former belonging to Col. Beauregard Beaucoupmots, publisher of the New Orleans *Picaroon-Statesman* and the Reverend Mother Emeritus' most ardent admirer, the latter belonging to Colonel de la Chevaux.

Neither vehicle, unfortunately, was appropriate transportation for Teddy Roosevelt. There was no way, obviously, that Teddy Roosevelt could be induced to climb the steel ladder to mount the swamp buggy, and although everybody pushed and shoved to the best of their ability, Teddy Roosevelt's broad shoulders just wouldn't squeeze through the doors of Colonel Beaucoupmot's limousine.

It was necessary to summon another vehicle, and while the party awaited its arrival, they stood in the shade beneath the wing of the airplane, a Chevaux Petroleum Boeing 747, sipping Sazerac cocktails and being serenaded by the Bayou Perdu Council, Knights of Columbus Marching Band.

There had been, truth to tell, several little misunderstandings both en route to New Orleans and once they arrived. The bandmaster of the Bayou Perdu Council, Knights of Columbus Marching Band had only to set eyes on Teddy Roosevelt to realize the animal was just what the band needed, far better than the two wild-cats and three goats with gilded horns they were presently utilizing as marching mascots.

'Hey, pop,' he said, 'what'll you take for that ugly hairy cow of yours?'

'Who you calling "pop"?' Uncle Hiram had responded.

'I'll give you a hundred bucks, old timer,' the bandmaster replied.

'Scalp him, Sitting Buffalo,' Uncle Hiram had replied. 'I don't want to get my new duds dirty.'

As the New Orleans contingent had gone from the

72

Dallas Airport to Texas Stadium, there to watch the Saints-Cowboys game, there had been an automobile accident involving their lead vehicle and the 1957 Cadillac hearse in which Sitting Buffalo, Teddy Roosevelt and Uncle Hiram had been running away from the Texas Rangers.

It was there that Uncle Hiram had first spotted Esther Flanagan, RN, and fallen helplessly, hopelessly in love with her.* The Bayou Perdu Council, Knights of Columbus had of course seen it as their clear duty to hide Uncle Hiram, Sitting Buffalo and Teddy Roosevelt from the minions of the law and had done so.

During this period, Uncle Hiram had confided in the Reverend Mother his affection for Nurse Flanagan. The idea had a certain appeal to the Reverend Mother. Here she was, only a few months older than her old friend Esther, and with two husbands behind her. Poor old Esther was yet to make that first march to the altar. It wasn't fair.

'Clothes make the man, Hiram,' the Reverend Mother had said, and then had taken him to an establishment known as Neiman-Marcus in Dallas, where she had outfitted him in, as he said, 'new duds,' and run him through the Neiman-Marcus Gentleman's Tonsorial Salon. Although she had not been presented with a bill for Neiman-Marcus' services, the Reverend Mother intended to pay for what services had been rendered from the Reverend Mother Emeritus' Discretionary Fund. 'You're a worthy cause, Hiram,' she said to him, 'if I've ever seen one.'

Sitting Buffalo had been dissuaded, not without difficulty, from scalping the bandmaster on the plane by Rev. Mother Emeritus, who had given him a half gallon of Old White Stagg Blended Kentucky Bourbon as a consolation prize.

* This love at first sight was not reciprocal, probably because, truth to tell, Uncle Hiram had acquired sort of an *aura de bison* during the long ride from the old T Bar X to Dallas, and also because Nurse Flanagan was not at all pleased to be addressed by Sitting Buffalo as Fat Redheaded Squaw.

And when they arrived at New Orleans Moissant Airport, Col. Beauregard Beaucoupmots had, perhaps naturally, come to the erroneous conclusion that the large English gentleman in the regimental moustache was hotly in pursuit of the lady he called Miss Margaret. (Rev. Mother Emeritus had outfitted Uncle Hiram from the racks of the Olde London Town Shoppe. After the Tonsorial Salon had reduced his Wild Bill Hickock coiffure and beard to no more than a closely cropped moustache, Uncle Hiram looked, in his suit, bowler hat and umbrella, as if he were a member of the House of Lords about to pay his respects to Her Majesty the Queen.)

But that, too, was straightened out, and eventually a flatbed truck arrived, Teddy Roosevelt was loaded aboard, and the party proceeded to the suite Colonel de la Chevaux maintained in the Royal Orleans Hotel for just such unexpected contingencies.

Chapter Seven

'You and your big mouth,' Trapper John said to Hawkeye when they had concluded their conversation with Mr
Matthew Q. Framingham VI of the Framingham
Theosophical Foundation. 'You and your "It's better to
marry than to burn"!'

'The way they were hanging on to each other,' Hawkeye replied, 'I was afraid they were going to spontane-
ously ignite. And who are you to talk? You and your
"Love is what makes the world go 'round." '

'Well, it does,' Trapper John said, somewhat lamely.
'Tell him, Esther.'

'Leave me out of this,' Esther said. 'After what
happened to me in Texas, I don't have any compassion
left over for you.'

'You mean what Sitting Buffalo called you?' Trapper
John asked. 'I realize that some people might think Fat
Redheaded Squaw is insulting, Esther, but I'm sure
Sitting Buffalo intended it as a compliment. He did give
you his bow and arrow. That certainly indicates he likes
you.'

'I mean that rum-soaked buddy of his,' Esther said.
'That smelly old cowboy telling me he loved me.'

'I don't think Uncle Hiram is as old as you think,
Esther,' Hawkeye said.

'With his hair and beard down to his waist, it's hard
to tell,' Trapper John said.

'He's a dirty old man, that's what he is,' Esther said,
with finality. 'If you shaved his beard off and gave him a

75

haircut, you'd have a dirty old man with a haircut and a shave.'

'Hot Lips likes him,' Hawkeye said.

'He was wearing pants, wasn't he? That's good enough for Hot Lips. Let her have him.'

'None of this is solving our problem with the widow Babcock,' Trapper John said. 'What we need, Esther, is some of your profound feminine insight.'

'See you around, Doc,' Esther said, draining her martini and heading for the door. 'I'm off to Montreal.'

'Montreal? Why Montreal?'

The reply came before Esther could stop it. She had had no intention of making public what was the most interesting development in her life to happen in a long time. But now the truth escaped her lips as if it had a life of its own.

'It just so happens, Trapper John, that I have a gentleman admirer in Montreal.'

'No kidding?'

'I wouldn't kid about something like that,' Esther replied. 'He's connected with the government of the province of Quebec. In a communications capacity.'

'You've got a French-Canadian bureaucrat on the string?' Hawkeye asked.

'The only reason I haven't thrown this gin bottle at you, Hawkeye,' Esther replied, 'is because I am a lady, and because my feminine instinct tells me that this Widow Babcock is really going to fix your wagon, and fix it good. You just don't go around telling Mother's only child that it's better to marry than to burn.'

'What about you, Esther?' Trapper John said. 'You got a little glow going with your French-Canadian bureaucrat?'

'Doctors,' Esther said, icily, drawing herself up to her full five-feet two-inches, 'should a medical emergency arise requiring my professional services, you may reach me at the La Belle France Motel in Montreal. Otherwise, you may expect to see me for Mr Oscar Goldberg's gall bladder, and not ten seconds before.'

'We're not going to jerk Oscar's gall bladder until next Monday morning,' Trapper John said.

'You certainly have a fine memory, Doctor,' Esther said.

'Then you mean you're going to leave us standing here naked and alone before the fury of the widow Babcock?' Hawkeye asked. 'Your friends and fellow healers?'

'You got it Doc,' Esther Flanagan said and, with that, her stiffly starched nurse's cap quivering slightly, she marched out of the office.

'I have the feeling that there's more to this than meets the eye,' Trapper John said.

'Hmmmm,' Hawkeye said, thoughtfully.

'I mean to say, that if she were just angry with us, she would have thrown the gin bottle,' Trapper John went on.

'Ummmmmm,' Hawkeye responded.

'Accompanied by one of those piquant scatological phrases she learned while sailing the briny blue with the Nurse Corps, United States Navy,' Trapper John said.

'What is *your* diagnosis, Doctor?' Hawkeye responded.

'I think there really is a gentleman admirer,' Trapper John said.

'Does that surprise you?' Hawkeye replied.

'Not at all,' Trapper John said. 'But I rather liked Uncle Hiram, especially after Hot Lips gave him a bath and a shave. He seemed just right for Esther.'

'I don't think she would have turned so red so quickly if there was no gentleman admirer,' Trapper John said.

'The real question, now that I have given it some thought,' Hawkeye said, 'is not whether or not there is a gentleman admirer, but whether or not Esther is running to him, or away from Uncle Hiram.'

'Pity Uncle Hiram's nothing more than a dirt-poor buffalo rancher,' Trapper John said. 'Say what you like, it has been my experience that a well-stuffed wallet frequently serves to make feminine hearts beat in three-quarter time.'

'Forgive me for being a shameless chauvinist,' Hawkeye said. 'But, so far as I'm concerned, better a poor American buffalo rancher than a French-Canadian bureaucrat, no matter how highly placed in the communications hierarchy, at least so far as our Esther is concerned.'

'My sentiments exactly,' Trapper John said. 'But do you know what's even better than a dirt-poor buffalo rancher?' He reached for the telephone.

'No,' Hawkeye said, thoughtfully. 'Unless perhaps a *formerly* dirt-poor buffalo rancher.'

'You really *are* the clever one,' Trapper John said and then spoke to the telephone. 'Hazel, please get me Col. Jean-Pierre de la Chevaux, wherever in the world he might be. Collect, of course.'

'You seem pretty confident that Horsey will have a job, a well-paying job, for him.'

'Of course, I am. It was "Hail, fellow, well met!" from the moment they saw each other. Didn't you see how, without, a word, they picked up that Texas Ranger and stuffed him, ten-gallon hat, cowboy boots and all, in the Dempster Dumpster?'

'That's true,' Hawkeye said. 'But Uncle Hiram may be too proud to accept Horsey's generosity.'

'Don't be silly,' Trapper John said. 'Uncle Hiram's in love. He said so. Men in love cannot afford pride. Uncle Hiram will just have to learn to live with shame and humiliation like the rest of us did.'

As the crow flies, it is less than 150 miles from Spruce Harbor, Maine, to Montreal in the Canadian province of Quebec. (By road, Maine roads being, as they are, under jurisdiction of politicians to whom the words 'straight line' are as incomprehensible as is the phrase 'saving the taxpayer's money', it is, of course, a good bit farther away.)

It was, in other words, close enough to become at first an odd notion, then a real possibility, then a tantalizing, attainable dream for Esther Flanagan, RN. Born in Boston, Esther had been, frankly, an ugly child and, in her teens, like so many of her kind, she had stuffed herself with food as compensation for her unhappiness, with the inevitable result that she had graduated from high school a fat, pimply, and unattractive female.

Most of the fat and most of the pimples (but not all of either) left her during her four years of training at Massachusetts General Hospital School of Nursing. Whatever else she was, Esther Flanagan, who at 21 had just entered her name on the Nurse's Register, was a pragmatist. She faced the fact that she was a short, red-headed, dumpy, bespectacled young woman, and that the odds against a knight in shining armour riding up on his white charger to carry her off, via a stop at the altar, to a vine-covered cottage and happiness everafter were very high indeed.

She had what she thought of as 'her nursing' and that, she told herself, was enough. Then the navy came along, with its offer to let her see the world while practising her profession. A month later, she reported aboard the US Navy Hospital, San Diego, California, as Lt. (jg) Esther Flanagan, Navy Nurse Corps.

The knight that came along, three years later, and who had seen beneath what he thought of as her rather cute pudginess to find a good woman, came in navy blue, riding a shining Grumman F4F fighter plane.

And six months after that, two weeks before he was to be reassigned to shore duty at Pensacola Naval Air Station (there was no point, they agreed, in getting married until he had some shore duty, and they could start out housekeeping), the gear collapsed on his F4F as he made an approach to the *Forrestal*, and there wasn't hardly enough left of him to bother burying.

She thought about leaving the navy then, and decided against it, and stayed in the navy. Before she knew it, she

79

had her twenty years in, and it was Comdr. Esther Flanagan, USN, chief of nursing services, Mediterranean Fleet, stationed aboard the hospital ship USS *Consolation*.

They piped her over the side in style. There was a farewell dinner in the wardroom of the carrier USS *Roosevelt*, and the admiral who offered the first of the toasts and recalled meeting Commander Flanagan at Guantanamo and Cabite and Pearl Harbor didn't seem to notice that what they were drinking was an intoxicating beverage forbidden aboard US Navy vessels.

And, when the banquet was over, the *Roosevelt* ship's band was formed on the flight deck lustily and then sadly playing 'Anchors Aweigh' as she boarded the Grumman twin turboprop transport that would fly her into retirement.

They were glad to have her back at Massachusetts General, and for a couple of months she enjoyed being on the beach, and in the little apartment she rented overlooking the Charles. But the good feeling didn't last long. For one thing, she missed the girls in the Navy Nurse Corps. For another, she learned that at Massachusetts General, they thought she was a little strange for being in the habit of dropping back afterward to see how her patients were doing. She had been hired as an operating room nurse, and that was all they expected – more importantly, wanted her to do. She wasn't even allowed to help pass gas. In the navy, she had been recognized to be one of the best gas-passers around.

And, while the apartment overlooking the Charles River was very nice, it was also very lonely.

Esther Flanagan, RN was no fool, and she knew that she was going to have to do something. The only problem was what. Certainly, the problem wasn't money. She had her navy pension, and it was a generous one, and she drew top pay as a nurse. And she had her bundle in the savings and loan. She could afford to do anything, go anywhere she wanted to. But she didn't know where to go. Where she really wanted to go was back in the navy, but that was out of the question. That part of her life had ended on the flight deck of the *Roosevelt* when she saluted the colours for the last time and the officer of the deck had given Commander Flanagan permission to leave the ship.

And then Sister Saint Francis of Assisi of the Convent of Saint Peter & Saint Paul had been brought in to Massachusetts General. The good sister was in bad shape, and they should have cut her immediately, but the good sister wasn't in any mood to be cut until she had talked to her brother, even after the gravity of her situation had been carefully explained to her. Her brother was in Rome, but was leaving immediately for Boston.

'My brother, Nurse Flanagan,' Sister Saint Francis said, with quiet pride, 'is an archbishop. The gossip has it that he knows His Holiness himself, personally.'

The same gossip had apparently reached the archdiocese of Boston, for when the archbishop arrived at Logan Field, he was greeted by the cardinal himself, who told him that, in addition to his prayers, he was offering the use of his limousine and any other facility of the archdiocese at his disposal so that the good sister could be nursed back to health.

Flanagan, who had (to hell with what the others thought of her; she recognized Sister Saint Francis as another lonely woman) been spending long hours with Sister Saint Francis, was there when the archbishop arrived, accompanied by his personal secretary.

'Your Eminence,' Sister Saint Francis said.

'Knock that off, Kathleen, I'm your brother John,' the archbishop said, bending over his sister to kiss her on the cheek. 'How are you feeling?'

'Not too well,' she said. 'I'm prepared to meet Saint Peter.'

'Don't get too anxious,' the archbishop had replied. 'That's not your decision to make.'

'Nurse Flanagan told me the truth when I asked her,'

Sister Saint Francis said. 'I'm in bad shape, Johnny.'

'Well, that may be,' he said. 'But we won't know for sure until some friends of mine have a look at you. They're on their way at this very moment.'

'And who are they, Johnny?'

'You remember when they took my lung, Kathleen?' the archbishop asked. 'I was in worse shape than you are now.'

'I remember, Johnny,' she said.

'The same two doctors,' the archbishop said. 'And it's not only my opinion that they're the finest surgeons around, but that of the Reverend Mother Bernadette of Lourdes, as well. And she's the chief of staff of the Gates of Heaven Hospital, so she knows what she's talking about.'

After that, Esther Flanagan, RN was not quite prepared for what she got. Instead of two solemn-appearing senior surgeons of the type one would think would be intimates of an archbishop was a tall chap in a plaid sweater and knickers and a slightly more stocky chap in a sweat shirt bearing the likeness of Ludwig von Beethoven, worn over a pair of rather fraying khakis.

They burst as quietly as they knew how into Sister Saint Francis' room where, in turn, they each picked up His Eminence the archbishop and kissed him wetly on the forehead.

'Dago Red,' the taller one said, 'we're sorry we took so long.'

'Hawkeye was chasing a small white ball with a weighted stick,' the other one said. 'And I, Dago Red, was communing with nature, and it took some time to find us.'

'I'm glad to see the both of you,' the archbishop said.

'What did he call you?' Sister Saint Francis said.

'A little nickname, Kathleen,' the archbishop said.

'I could have sworn he called you Dago Red,' the good sister said.

'Who is this lady?' the taller one said.

'Hawkeye, this is Esther Flanagan, who's been sort of keeping an eye on my sister.'

'I don't want to be rude, miss,' the taller one said, 'but Dr McIntyre and I would like to examine Sister Saint Francis now. Take Dago Red with you and wait outside, please?'

'*Dr* McIntyre?' Flanagan had asked, incredulously. 'And that's *Nurse* Flanagan to you, Slim.'

'Nurse Flanagan,' the archbishop said quickly. 'This is Dr Benjamin F. Pierce and Dr John F. X. McIntyre.'

'What kind of a nurse?' Dr Pierce had enquired.

'I'm an operating room nurse,' Flanagan had replied.

'OK, you can stick around. You get out of here, Dago Red.'

'I'll wait in the corridor,' the archbishop said.

While they were examining Sister Saint Francis, the chief of vascular surgery came into the room. He stood watching silently as the examination progressed.

When it was over, Dr McIntyre met the eyes of Dr Pierce. Then Dr Pierce turned to Sister Saint Francis.

'If you're willing to have a couple of heathens cut a hole in you, Sister,' he said, 'I think we can have you back in the convent in about two weeks. No guarantees, of course.'

'I'm not exactly a heathen, Sister,' Dr McIntyre said. 'More on the order of a backslider, actually.'

Dr Pierce went to the door and summoned the archbishop.

'I just told your sister, Dago Red, that if she'll let a couple of heathens have at her, we can probably, no guarantee, have her back in the convent in two weeks.'

'Thank you, Hawkeye,' the archbishop said, hugging him.

'You'll vouch for these . . . gentlemen, Johnny?' Sister Saint Francis asked, rather doubtfully.

'With my life, Kathleen,' the archbishop said.

'Will you set up a team for us, Charley?' Dr McIntyre said to the chief of vascular surgery. 'Right now?'

'I don't know what I can do right now,' the chief of vascular surgery replied. 'Would you like me to assist?'

'I thought you'd never ask,' Hawkeye said. 'Yeah, Charley, please. Then all we'll need is a good gas-passer, and a head OR nurse.'

'You've got your head OR nurse,' Esther Flanagan heard herself saying, in violation of the protocol.

Dr Pierce looked at her for a moment.

'OK, Red, you're on,' he said. 'Come along with us, we'll show you the pictures, and how we're going to adjust the little pieces inside the good sister.'

Five hours later, Esther Flanagan, RN was paid what she considered two of the nicest compliments she had ever been paid.

They were in intensive care, waiting for Sister Saint Francis to come out of anaesthesia, when Dr Pierce suddenly looked at her and said, 'Incidentially, Red, you know your business. Thanks a lot.'

'That's right, Red,' Dr McIntyre said. 'You're not bad at all. If you should ever decide to chuck this joint, look us up.'

Sister Saint Francis of Assisi returned to her convent ten days after her surgical procedure. Nurse Flanagan watched her ride off in the taxi and then went to the parking lot and, armed with a road map, set out for Spruce Harbor, Maine.

When she walked into the lobby of the Spruce Harbor Medical Centre, Hazel Schultz Heidenheimer, the telephone operator/receptionist, told her that Drs Pierce and McIntyre were in conference and could not be disturbed.

'I'll wait,' Esther Flanagan replied.

Hazel Schultz Heidenheimer, who liked Esther Flanagan at sight, and fully aware that Drs Pierce and McIntyre might continue in conference until suppertime, ignored the blue CONFERENCE IN SESSION light on her switchboard and rang the telephone in the office of the chief of surgery.

'There's a lady waiting to see you,' she said. 'She won't tell me what she wants. Her name is Flanagan.'

'Has she got red hair?' Trapper John asked.

'Yes.'

'Send her down, Hazel, please,' Trapper John said.

Esther Flanagan two minutes later walked into the office of the Spruce Harbor Medical Centre chief of surgery for the first time. Trapper John opened the door for her. The chief of surgery, a martini glass in one hand, was in the act of throwing a dart from the other at the photograph of a man in the uniform of an army doctor.

'Glad to see ya, Red,' Trapper John said. 'I don't suppose we could interest you in a little martini?'

'Don't mind if I do,' Esther Flanagan said. She did not approve of drinking on medical premises, of course, but she needed, she realized, a little liquored courage.

'I knew you were our kind of people,' Trapper John said, handing her a martini.

'Be with you in a minute, Red,' Hawkeye called. 'Just as soon as I let old Frank have a dart in the eye.'

He proceeded to do just that.

'Now, what brings you to this crossroads of the world, and what, in addition to the martini, can we do for you?' Hawkeye asked.

'I'm looking for a job,' Esther blurted.

'Here?' Trapper John asked, surprised.

'I've checked this place out,' Esther said. 'You've got a good reputation.'

'You refer, of course, to the hospital,' Hawkeye said.

'Dr McIntyre said if I should ever chuck Massachusetts General, I should look him up,' Esther blurted, and then drained her martini. 'Well, I chucked it. As of zero eight hundred.'

Hawkeye drained his martini, too, and then went and pulled the dart from Maj. Frank Burns' photograph, where it had landed in the eye, before speaking.

'Zero eight hundred?' he asked. 'Could I do the Sherlock Holmes bit and cleverly deduce that sometime in your life you have been around the military?'

'Around the navy,' Esther Flanagan said. 'Commander, retired.'

'Two points for Red,' Trapper John said. 'One for her performance in the OR when we cut Dago Red's sister, and one for naval service.'

'Three points and you get elected mayor,' Hawkeye said, and picked up his telephone. 'Hazel, get me Crumbum* on the line,' he ordered. He pushed the button that turned on the amplifier, so that both sides of the conversation could be heard.

'T. Alfred Crumley, Sr here,' a somewhat nasal voice announced.

'How they hanging, Crumbum?' Hawkeye enquired.

'I've told you, and I've *told* you,' Mr Crumley said. 'That's Crumley. Crum-ley.'

'Right you are,' Trapper John replied. 'Sorry about that. Tell me, Crumbum, how are we fixed, personnel-wise, for nurse personnel, senior type-wise?'

'If I understand your question correctly, Doctor,' Mr Crumley replied, 'and God knows how hard it is to understand anything you say, you want to know our position, nurse-wise? In particular, so far as senior-level personnel are concerned?'

'You got it,' Hawkeye replied.

'The only thing we have available is that frankly dreadful job of chief of nursing training.'

'Why is it dreadful?'

'Well, for one thing, Doctor, between us, the money is lousy. For another, the incumbent must reside in the student nurses' dormitory. That alone has caused the last seven incumbents to depart, three of them hysterical. And, for a third, as if the first two aren't bad enough, the incumbent's hours are simply ghastly. The poor thing has to work sixty hours a week just to stay even.'

'I'll take it,' Esther Flanagan said.

'Take down the help wanted sign, Crumbum,' Hawkeye said. 'I've just found you a highly qualified sucker.'

* Dr Pierce here referred to T. Alfred Crumley, administrator of the Spruce Harbor Medical Centre.

Chapter Eight

Hawkeye and Trapper John, skilled practioners of the fine art of hospital bureaucratic chicanery, realized that Esther Flanagan would be a good person to have around. The important thing to do was get her officially on the payroll. Once she had been officially employed, certain changes could be made in the exact nature of her employment.

In other words, they wanted her in the operating room. She would work in the operating room no matter what her job title was on the Personnel Distribution & Assignment Chart, which occupied all of one wall in Crumbum's office.

She joined them the very next morning, as a matter of fact, even before there was time for her to return to the apartment overlooking the Charles and start packing. But Drs Pierce and McIntyre had been in error, and so had Mr Crumley, who had feared when he welcomed Esther aboard that he had been done in by his surgical staff once again. Esther did not just become Hawkeye's and Trapper John's more or less private Queen Empress of the operating room. She moved into a small apartment in the student nurses' dormitory and quickly brought order out of that chaos. (She had, after all, many years of being senior officer aboard various bachelor officers' quarters [female] all over the world. Handling young females was no problem at all for her.)

Similarly, putting a little order into the training of student nurses was not much of a problem for a woman who had been the chief of nursing services,

US Mediterranean Fleet.

When the position of chief of nursing services for the Spruce Harbor Medical Centre became open (the incumbent retired), Esther Flanagan, RN was the natural choice for the position, not only because she was recommended by the departing chief of nursing services, the chief of surgery, and the hospital administrator, but also because she announced she would continue running the student nurses' dormitory and their training as well.

It was, for her, very much like still being in the navy. Her every waking hour was full of interesting things to do. The unwritten rule was that when anything interesting (in other words, a difficult procedure) was going on in the OR, Esther Flanagan would scrub. The respect in which she came to be held by the doctorial staff was reflected in their willingness to teach the student nurses. Keeping them happy, bright and reasonably entitled to wear white on their ultimate wedding days occupied what would have been normally her off-duty hours.

And the prestige was there, too. She became the first woman admitted to the chief of surgery's daily conferences on a permanent basis. The only other woman ever to be permitted behind the CONFERENCE IN SESSION sign was the legendary latter-day Florence Nightingale with whom Dr Pierce and Dr McIntyre had served in the 4077th MASH during the Korean War, a fellow practitioner of the nursing art named Lieutenant Colonel 'Hot Lips' Houlihan Wachauf Wilson, RN, USA, retired.

No one was at all surprised when Commander Flanagan, retired, and Colonel Wilson, retired, met; that the two almost immediately became fast friends. They had, after all, a good deal in common. But there was one thing, Esther Flanagan came to sadly (and very secretly) consider, that they did not have in common. Hot Lips had men at her beck and call, men presenting her with candy, flowers and booze, men to gratify her every hunger. Esther Flanagan was still as manless as she had been when a 'husky stylish stout' in high school.

One day there came into Esther's hand a full-colour brochure put out by the Canadian government's *Bureau pour l'Encouragement du Tourisme*. This brochure dealt with the manifold charms of Montreal, in the province of Quebec.

'A little bit of romantic France, but just across the border,' the caption beneath a hand-holding couple seated at a candlelit table said.

'Old-world romance and charm in the new world,' read another caption, this one showing a hand-holding couple, her head resting against his broad manly shoulder, as they looked up at the Bonsecours Church (built 1771). Although the caption didn't say so, Esther was absolutely convinced she was looking at the Bonsecours Church because it had been, or was going to be, the site of their joining together in holy matrimony.

That alone would probably have been enough to have had Esther look fondly upon Montreal, but a third picture, showing a middle-aged woman having her hand kissed by a very distinguished-appearing gentleman of similar age, bore this caption: 'Montreal is above all a friendly place, where you are a stranger but once.'

That made her first trip to Montreal as inevitable as the dawn following the night.

At first it had been, frankly, something of a disappointment to her. She arrived in the little bit of romantic France just across the border, as night fell and the neon sign in front of the Holiday Inn in which she was to stay was just flickering on. Determined to savour as much of Montreal's romantic old-world charm as she could, and as quickly as possible, she passed up the Holiday Inn restaurant, and set out in search of a candlelit table, and the *Cuisine Française* the brochure had told her she could find. Two hours later, after encountering nothing but hippies, souvenir stands, X-rated movie houses and hot-dog dispensaries, she gave up the search and wound up eating Kentucky Fried Chicken in a very familiar-looking structure that displayed the likeness of the founder on the roof.

Coming to the not-very-flattering conclusion that she'd been had by the *Bureau pour l'Encouragement du Tourisme*, Esther had reacted characteristically.

'To hell with it,' she said, to no one in particular, and marched into the Joan of Arc 12-Lanes No-Waiting Bowling Alley & Cocktail Lounge on Avenue Charles de Gaulle, not far from the Champs de Mars municipal parking lot.

Esther had once led the Guantanamo Bay Naval Station 'Florence Nightingales' to a smashing victory over the bowling team from the chief petty officer's mess, and she knew that a couple of lines of bowling, with the pins scattering noisily, plus a couple of beers, would, so to speak, restore her normal cheerful spirits.

It was at the Joan of Arc Cocktail Lounge that Esther met her gentleman admirer. She was sitting at the far end of the bar (so as to make it perfectly clear, should the question arise, that she was in the establishment to have a couple of beers, period) about to finish her third beer and return to her solo bowling for another couple of lines when the bartender slid another glass of suds before her.

'I didn't order that,' Esther said.

'Courtesy of the gentleman at duh far end of duh bar,' the bartender said.

Esther looked in the direction, already sucking in her breath to firmly announce that she was perfectly able to buy her own beer, thank you, when she got a good look at the gentleman and became, for one of the few times in her life, speechless.

Either they were putting something in this Canadian beer they didn't put in beer in the States, and she was a lot higher than she felt, or the gentleman at the far end of the bar was the very same distinguished-appearing gentleman in the brochure from the *Bureau pour l'En-Encouragement du Tourisme*, the one in the picture with the caption line 'Montreal is above all a friendly place, where you are a stranger but once.'

She closed her eyes and shook her head to clear her vision and looked again. This was all that it took to see M. Henri Flambeau come quickly down the bar to her.

M. Flambeau had noticed Esther Flanagan the moment she walked into the Joan of Arc 12-Lanes No-Waiting Bowling Alley & Cocktail Lounge, examined her carefully and initially dismissed her as beneath his notice. She did not, in other words, look like the type of woman Henri Flambeau was looking for, which is to say, a rich and lonely tourist.

And then he had just happened to notice how Esther had paid for her first beer, that is to say, with a hundred-dollar traveller's cheque torn from a rather thick little booklet of traveller's cheques which were probably, he judged professionally, of the same denomination.

'I hope, mademoiselle,' Henri Flambeau said to Esther Flanagan, 'that you will be able to find it in your heart to forgive my impulsiveness.'

He sounded, Esther realized, just like Jacques Costeau, the fish guy.

'Uh . . .' Esther said.

'I could think of no other way in which I might hope to make your acquaintance,' Henri Flambeau said.

'Uh . . .' Esther said again.

'And I could not help but notice that you somehow have become separated from your friends,' Henri Flambeau went on. 'Even as I have. That we were both, so to speak, alone.'

Esther drained her beer, having exhausted all she could think of to say.

'And it occurred to me that you might be kind enough, my treat of course, to bowl a line with me.'

'Don't mind if I do,' Esther replied. 'But dutch treat, of course.'

'I beg your pardon?'

'Dutch treat,' she repeated. 'We each pay our own way.'

'If you insist,' Henri Flambeau said.

Within the hour, they had bowled three lines. Esther had learned that it was indeed Henri Flambeau in the BPET brochure: 'They came to me and asked if I would pose for the picture,' he said. 'And I decided that I could not refuse. My country was calling me to service.'*

Esther also learned that M. Flambeau was a bachelor, and professionally associated with the Quebec provincial government in a communications capacity, both of which facts he was too modest to discuss.**

On the other hand, M. Flambeau learned a number of interesting things about Esther Flanagan. For one thing, in addition to her stack of traveller's cheques, she had a steady job. Having a steady job, especially a well-paying one, was something Henri always looked for in his lady friends. For another, giving her an attraction that grew by the minute, she had a pension. He had no idea how large the monthly retirement cheque of a commander, retired, of the United States Navy amounted to, but it was very likely a nice little sum indeed.

He also learned that Esther had yet to march to the altar, which told him that she should be handled with great care. (By the end of the second line of bowling, M. Flambeau had realized that he was quite as smitten with this Little American Duckling, as he thought of her, as he had been with his three previous wives; that she was a potential marriage partner rather than simply another fling for him.)

* While this was, in a sense, true, M. Flambeau did not feel it necessary to add that the reason they had come and asked him to pose for the picture was that a dossier of photographs of him had been available at the Montreal Models Registry, together with his price: $15 per hour (negotiable).

** Again, this was the truth, but not the whole truth. Flambeau was a bachelor, but only in the sense that his third wife had just obtained a divorce from him on grounds of non-support. His professional association in a communications capacity with the Quebec provincial government saw him daily occupying the third window from the front in the Montreal post' office, where he had full charge of money orders and international postal reply coupons.

That thought was clinched when she told him where she lived and worked and that she had an automobile. It was only a few hours' drive for her to come to Montreal. M. Flambeau found it difficult to leave Montreal. There were governmental reasons, he told Esther, and there were, although he didn't go into them. He had, in fact, been bluntly told by the judge of domestic relations that the next time he left Montreal without permission, the judge would conclude that he was again trying to avoid alimony and child-support payments and the judge would be forced to toss him into the slammer again.

The longer Henri Flambeau knew Esther Flanagan, the more he learned about her financial position, the greater his conviction grew that here, finally, was the woman of his dreams, the woman who could, with relatively minor effort on her part, support him in the manner to which he would like to be accustomed. Her pension, a little research in the Montreal Public Library's USA (formerly American) Collection told him, would be more than enough to pay all of his alimony and child-support obligations, with a nice little piece of change left over. By driving across the border, and making a station-to-station call from a phone booth and identifying himself as the Greater Main Credit Bureau, he had been able to get a chap named T. Alfred Crumley, Sr. to inform him just how much Esther Flanagan was paid as chief of nursing services of the Spruce Harbor Medical Centre.

Marriage was the obvious answer. Esther had no way of knowing this, of course (although she had her hopes), but Henri Flambeau had already decided to pop the question, to ask Esther to become his bride. He didn't want to blow it, of course, and made rather elaborate plans for the great occasion.

As Esther Flanagan approached the Canadian-American border in her navy grey Ford, another lady, to whom the idea of marriage was, at least so far as her

Precious Babykins was concerned, unspeakably outrageous approached Boston's Logan Field in her silver grey Model 60 Learjet.

The Learjet touched down, and then taxied to the terminal building, where its sole passenger was escorted to the VIP waiting lounge.

'Ah, there you are,' said the tall, still-blonde, still-attractive Mrs Josephine Babcock to the short, rather purple-haired lady wearing eyeglasses, each spectacle of which was a good five inches in diameter. 'Have you been waiting long?'

'Only four hours, Mrs Babcock,' Sydney Prescott replied, flashing her choppers and gesturing with the eighteen-inch cigarette holder in which smouldered a freshly lit Cognoscenti cigarette. (Another fine product of Burton Babcock & Company, Cognoscenti cigarettes are advertised as being for those in the know. Exactly what is known is not specified.)

'Well, your time isn't really very valuable, when you get right down to it,' Josephine said. 'And I'm sure you were glad to get out of New York City.'

Sydney Prescott smiled even wider. 'Sydney Prescott stands ever alert to be of service to Burton Babcock & Company generally and you, specifically, Madame Chairperson,' she said.

'In that case, you can start by getting rid of that horrible-smelling cigarette,' Mrs Babcock said. 'It's enough to make one toss one's cookies.'

Sydney Prescott ground out the offending butt as Mrs Babcock held her nose.

'What in the hell was that, anyway?' Mrs Babcock enquired. 'If I didn't know better, I'd think someone was slipping *soja hispida Babcockisis* into the mixture again.'

'It was a Cognoscenti, Mrs Babcock,' Sydney Prescott replied. 'I was just trying to show my corporate loyalty.'

'Next time, try some Old Mountain Lion Chewing Tobacco,' Mrs Babcock ordered.

Sydney Prescott wrote this little suggestion down in the notebook she habitually carried for just that purpose.

'And now, Madame Chairperson, how may I be of service?' she asked.

'The thing is, Prescott,' Mrs Babcock said, 'I have a personal problem which you may possibly be of some use in solving. It's a strange problem, and you're a strange woman, don't you see?'

'Tell me more,' Sydney Prescott said.

'To get right to the point,' Mrs Babcock began, 'let me begin by saying that if anything said in this room leaves this room, not only will you never get another dime of Burton Babcock & Company's business, but I will personally tear your purple hair out down to the last grey root. Do we understand each other?'

'Perfectly, Madame Chairperson.'

'Very well then,' Mrs Babcock went on. 'The problem is this. My son, Burton Babcock IV, my only child, Mama's Precious Babykins, has fallen under the influence of an undesirable young woman.'

'I see,' Sydney Prescott said.

'Don't be absurd,' Mrs Babcock went on. 'I have barely begun. How could you possibly see?'

'As one woman to another,' Sydney Prescott said.

'Don't presume, Prescott,' Josephine replied. 'You're a woman. I'm a lady.'

'Please go on,' Sydney Prescott said. 'How is she undesirable?'

'Well, for one thing, so far as I know, she doesn't have a dime. She's obviously after Precious Babykins for his money.'

'Perhaps, forgive me, Madame Chairperson, she's after his, you know, his body. Your Precious Babykins is one hell of a man you know.'

'Bite your tongue, you dirty-minded middle-aged sex maniac; my Precious Babykins is practically virginal.'

'Of course, he is,' Sydney Prescott quickly backtracked. 'I'd forgotten that Bubba was a Green Beret. Everyone knows that Green Berets are above that sort of thing.'

'Bubba assured me of that himself,' Josephine replied.

'But as his mother, I must honestly face the facts. He's his father's son, and his father, truth to tell, may he rest in peace, was a gloriously successful skirt chaser in his time. Before he met me, of course. But the genes are there, and one day, if, God forbid, it hasn't happened already, Precious Babykins is going to find out just what happens to female hearts when they see that massive chest, those steely biceps and those pearl white teeth.'

'Where did Precious Babykins meet this gold digger?' Sydney Prescott enquired.

'Get this straight, Prescott,' Josephine said. 'While he may be Precious Babykins to me, to you, he's either Mr Babcock or, perhaps, under those trying circumstances, Bubba.'

'Got you,' Sydney Prescott said. 'You were telling me where he met the gold digger?'

'Presumably at a football game,' Josephine said. 'Her one claim to cultural attainment is that she was a University of Texas Marching Band Pompon Girl.'

'I've seen them on television,' Sydney Prescott said. 'I remember when that sort of display was against the law.'

'Times have changed, Prescott,' Josephine said.

'And Bubba's infatuation for the gold digger is pretty serious?'

'Serious isn't the word,' Josephine said. 'He wants to marry her!'

'That's serious,' Sydney agreed. 'What sort of a girl is she?'

'I'll let you decide for yourself,' Josephine said. 'She's got a shape like a Greek goddess, she could pass Ann Lander's pencil test summa cum laude, and Bubba tells me she has all the makings of a first-class HALO jumper.'

The term HALO was one with which Sydney Prescott was not familiar. The mental image that popped into her mind was of boy and girl angels cavorting in shameless abandon among the clouds.

'A first-class HALO jumper?' she asked, just to be

sure she'd heard right.

'So he says,' Josephine said. 'At this very moment, while the sand runs rapidly through the hourglass of the time we have remaining to stop this doomed union, Precious Babykins is jumping her, over and over again, at Fort Bragg.'

'My God, it's later than you led me to believe!' Sydney Prescott said.

'Let me get to the bottom line, Prescott,' Josephine Babcock said. 'I frankly find you to be one of the most loathsome creatures I have ever encountered. However, it occurred to me that anyone with a mind devious enough to get all these millions of crazy ladies of the women's lib movement to start sniffing Old Billie Goat Snuff by the ton just possibly might be able to come up with some foul idea that would save my Precious Babykins from this blonde gold digger.'

'How nice of you to say so, Madame Chairperson.'

'If you can break this thing up, Prescott,' Josephine Babcock said. 'I which is to say, Burton Babcock & Company, would be very grateful. Very grateful indeed. Need I say more?'

'Yes, I think you need to,' Sydney Prescott said. 'Now that you mention it.'

'I'll give you the Cognoscenti cigarette advertising account for openers,' Josephine said. 'That's a 6.6 million-dollar account, you know.'

'Put your worried mother's heart to rest, Madame Chairperson,' Sydney Prescott replied. 'Sydney Prescott will have this blonde digger on her way way back to the University of Texas Marching Band and her pompons before you know it. Unmarried, of course.'

'I had hoped to be able to count on you, Prescott,' Josephine Babcock said. 'And now I think you'd be better running along. The executive secretary of the Matthew Q. Framingham Theosophical Foundation is also meeting me here.'

'Really?'

'My late husband, Precious Babykins' daddy, may he rest in peace, was a Framingham Fellow,' Josephine said, with quiet, if evident, pride. 'So you can see how embarrassing it would be for me if I were seen in your company.'

Chapter Nine

Rev. Mother Emeritus Margaret, of the God Is Love In All Forms Christian Church, Inc. was, if nothing else, a woman of the world. As such, although she liked him, she did rather question whether Hiram Jones's professed love for Esther Flanagan was indeed sincere, or whether, as the Reverend Mother thought of it, Esther were just a passing fanny.

She put his professed devotion to the test in the most meaningful way she knew. Accompanied by Colonel de la Chevaux, Sitting Buffalo and His Royal Highness, Sheikh Abdullah ben Abzug (Teddy Roosevelt having been left behind in Colonel de la Chevaux's suite in the Royal Orleans), she led Uncle Hiram on a tour of the French Quarter, starting out in Houlihan's Saloon,* right across the street from the Royal Orleans and working their way up Bourbon Street, down Royal Street, up Rue Toulouse and ending up in an establishment known as Lucky Pierre's.

There would be, the Reverend Mother Emeritus knew, in her wisdom, at each stop along the route ladies of spectacular physical proportions and no high morals worth mentioning. She was further aware that because of previous visits to the same establishments by ol' Abdullah, that he would be more than warmly welcomed back. Few French Quarter denizens were unaware that

---

* Both the proprietor of Houlihan's Saloon and high-ranking members of the GILIAFCC, Inc. ecclesiastical hierarchy flatly deny that Houlihan's Saloon was named after former Maj. Margaret Houlihan, Nurse Corps, US Army.

the bearded chap who spoke so little English was the fellow who had ridden through the Quarter in one of the picturesque horse-drawn buggies throwing diamonds and rubies at every female he saw who pleased his eye. Abdullah's ride had earned him, among the French Quarter Professional Girls Marching & Chowder Society the nickname 'The Pied Piper' for, by the time his wagon ride was over, more than four hundred 'professional' denizens (as well as a number of amateurs and semi-professionals) were following the buggy.

The ladies turned out as the Reverend Mother Emeritus had predicted, but Uncle Hiram had shown far more interest in booze than in the broads. The Reverend Mother had next decided that perhaps her presence had a restraining influence on him and, on a rather flimsy pretext,* returned to the Royal Orleans.

When, at four AM, only Colonel de la Chevaux had returned to the suite (he had, actually, been carried, back by four of New Orleans's finest), the Reverend Mother Emeritus came to the sad, if not unexpected, conclusion that Uncle Hiram had succumbed to the temptations of the flesh, and that his interest in Esther Flanagan was not, as she thought of it, sincere. She then went to bed.

At seven in the morning, as was her custom, the Reverend Mother Emeritus broke her fast at the Café du Monde (six *beignets*, a cup of coffee and two inches of Remy Martin brandy) near Jackson Square. Half-way through the second *beignet*,** the sound of music came to her. It was, she was sure, the familiar, rather gravelly voice of Uncle Hiram, in not-at-all unpleasant counterpoint to Sitting Buffalo's *basso profundo*. They were singing, 'I Want a Girl Just Like the Girl That Married Dear Old Dad.'

* She announced that she was afraid Teddy Roosevelt would become lonely at the hotel, even though they had left him tied to the balcony outside Horsey's suite, so that he could watch what the Reverend Mother called the weirdos promenading on Bourbon Street.
** A *beignet* is a French, or holeless, doughnut.

She had been rehearsing the little sermonlike talk she intended to deliver to Uncle Hiram, telling him that he would have to repent before he could even hope to gain Esther Flanagan's heart, and it seemed to her that this was as good a time to deliver the sermonette as she could hope for.

Following the sound of the music, she walked quickly up Rue Sainte Anne, turned right and found herself before the door to Lucky Pierre's. Inside she found His Royal Highness Sheikh Abdullah ben Abzug stretched out on the bar, and Uncle Hiram and Sitting Buffalo at the piano bar, the piano of which was being played by a rather nice-looking young fellow visibly on the point of exhaustion.

The pianist, Frankie by name, knew the Reverend Mother Emeritus.

'Thank God you're here, Hot Lips,' he said. 'Get me out of this!'

In a moment, she saw the problem. Uncle Hiram's trusty Colt .45 Single-Action Frontier revolver was lying on the piano. Every time the pianist started to stop playing, Uncle Hiram picked it up.

'How long have they been here, Frankie?' the Reverend Mother Emeritus asked.

'All night,' Frankie replied. 'They wouldn't leave, and they wouldn't let me play anything but "I Want a Girl Just Like the Girl That Married Dear Old Dad", "Miss You Since You Went Away, Dear" and something called "I'll Take You Home Again, Flanagan".'

'OK, Frankie,' the Reverend Mother said, 'Play "Good night, Sweetheart" and you can call it a day.'

'Can you handle this guy, Hot Lips?' Frankie asked, somewhat doubtfully.

'Trust me, Frankie,' the Reverend Mother said. 'Have I ever failed you before?'

Frankie segued into 'Good night, Sweetheart' and Uncle Hiram, whose head was rather sagging over his glass, raised it, and then raised his trusty Colt .45 to point it at the pianist

'Play it again, Frankie,' Uncle Hiram said.

'Put that thing down, Hiram,' the Reverend Mother said.

Uncle Hiram noticed her for the first time.

'Evening, Reverend Mother, ma'am,' he said politely. 'Would you-all care to join in on a chorus of "I'll Take You Home Again, Flanagan"?'

'Thank you, no, Hiram,' the Reverend Mother said.

'How about "Miss You Since You Went Away, Dear"?' Uncle Hiram asked.

'There won't be time for that, Hiram,' Hot Lips said. 'We're going to take a little trip.'

'Zat so?' he asked, curiously. 'Where and when and why?'

'We're going to Maine,' Hot Lips said.

'The hell I am,' Uncle Hiram replied. 'Over my dead Texas body we are.'

'Just as soon as we get some coffee into you, and you into the shower,' the Reverend Mother went on with that infuriating boundless patience and tolerance that is the earmark of certain members of the clergy.

'The only thing I'm going to get into,' Uncle Hiram announced, rather belligerently, 'is another bottle of this Old White Stagg Blended Kentucky Bourbon.' He looked around for the bartender. The gentleman was nowhere in sight. In fact, with the exception of the party at the piano bar, and His Royal Highness snoring on the bar, the establishment was deserted.

When he couldn't see the bartender, Uncle Hiram decided he was in the back room and required summoning. He thumbed back the hammer of the Colt .45 and pulled the trigger, shattering the crystal chandelier over the piano.

'To see Miss Esther Flanagan,' the Reverend Mother went on placidly.

'Wake up the Arab, Sitting Buffalo,' Uncle Hiram said. 'We're off to Maine.'

His Royal Highness had, in fact, been awakened by the sound of the chandelier pieces crashing to the floor. He was now sitting up on the bar.

'Ah,' he said. 'Hot Lips! Up yours, Reverend Mother!'

'Up yours, Abdullah,' the Reverend Mother replied with a warm smile. 'Now pay the bill, and we'll all go to see the Sainted Chancre Mechanic and Trapper John.'*

His Royal Highness threw a five-hundred-dollar bill on the bar and raised his hand to the pianist. 'You mother wears army boots, Frankie!' he cried fondly, and then threw him another five-hundred-dollar bill. 'Let's get this goddamned circus on the road!' he said, finally, and marched out the door.

'That's my kind of an Arab,' Uncle Hiram confided to the Reverend Mother Emeritus, draping an affectionate arm around her shoulder. 'Holds his booze almost as good as a Texan.'

About an hour later, the telephone rang in the Spruce Harbor Medical Centre.

'Esther Flanagan, RN chief of nursing services, please,' the person-to-person operator said. 'Margaret H. W. Wilson, RN, chief of nursing instruction, the Ms Prudence MacDonald Memorial School of Nursing, is calling.'

'Sorry, Esther ain't here,' Hazel Schultz Heidenheimer said.

'Your party, madame, cannot be reached at this time,' the operator reported to Nurse Houlihan. Nurse Houlihan was at the moment engaged in spraying a heavy

---

* The Reverend Mother was quite aware that what few words of English the Sheikh spoke he had learned, at the knee, so to speak, of Boris Alexandrovich Korsky-Rimsakov, the World's Greatest Opera Singer, who often spoke the picturesque phrases he had learned as a Browning Automatic Rifleman with the 223rd Infantry. 'Sainted Chancre Mechanic' was the fond appellation applied to Dr Benjamin Franklin Pierce, FACS, by Maestro Korsky-Rimsakov.

stream of ice-cold water on Uncle Hiram, while Colonel de la Chevaux held him propped up against the stall shower in his suite.

'In that case, I will speak with either Dr. B. F. Pierce or John F. X. McIntyre,' Hot Lips called. (The phone, equipped with one of those clever hands-off devices, was in the adjacent room.)

'That you, Hot Lips?' Hazel enquired. 'Sounds like you're talking in a shower.'

'How perceptive of you, Hazel,' Hot Lips replied. 'And how is Ace?'

'I *am* sorry,' the operator said. 'If you persist in talking personally rather than professionally to the operator I shall be forced by Ma Bell's immutable rules to charge you whatever the tariff will allow.'

'Damn the expense,' Hot Lips called out. 'Get Hawk-eye on the horn, Hazel, will you?'

'He's cutting, Hot Lips. He and Trapper John. Is it important? If it is, I'll ring the operating room.'

'No, not really,' Hot Lips said. 'Just tell him that Horsey and I, Sitting Buffalo, Uncle Hiram, and Abdullah are going to be in the neighbourhood, and we thought we'd just drop by and say hello. Tell him not to tell Esther. We'll surprise her.'

'You'll surprise her all right,' Hazel replied. 'She ain't here. She's in Montreal.'

As she said this, however, Uncle Hiram groaned as the shock of the ice-cold water finally penetrated the thick clouds of booze. Hot Lips didn't hear the reply.

'You get that, Hazel?' she called.

'I got it,' Hazel said. 'Just as soon as they're free, I'll tell them.'

'Give my love to Ace,' Hot Lips cried out. Then, 'Turn him around, Horsey, we'll baste the other side awhile.'

'If we have to do the same thing to Sitting Buffalo and Abdullah, we'll be here all day,' Horsey protested.

'They can sleep it off on the plane,' Hot Lips said.

'But Hiram has to be bright-eyed and bushy-tailed when he first sees Esther again. First impressions count you know.'

'The first time Esther saw him, it was hard to tell him from his buffalo,' Horsey said. 'The one tied to the balcony, I mean. Not the one with the feather.'

'Think positively, Horsey!' Hot Lips chided him. 'Now he looks like an English gentleman. A drunk, out-of-his-mind, soaking-wet English gentleman, maybe, but an English gentleman.'

Ida-Sue and Alamo Jones received an interim report of the ongoing investigations into the mysterious disappearances of Miss Scarlett Rose-Marie Jones and Mr Hiram Jones in the congressional suite of the Dallas Hilton Hotel. Chief Deputy Inspector Wilbur J. Hawkins of the Super Sleuth Private Detective & Anti-Cattle Rustling Security Services, Inc. personally delivered the report.

'We have ascertained, beyond any shadow of a doubt,' Chief Deputy Inspector Hawkins reported, 'that Wild West Beanos, or at least the advertising agency for Wild West Beanos, are in this mysterious double disappearance up to their ears.'

'What the hell is he talking about, Ida-Sue?' Congressman Alamo Jones enquired. 'What the hell are Wild West Beanos?'

'They are a variety of *soja hispida*, specifically *soja hispida Babcockisis*,' Hawkins replied.

'I'm sorry I asked,' Ida-Sue said. 'What has this stuff got to do with my beloved baby daughter and crazy Uncle Hiram?'

'I'm getting to that, ma'am,' Chief Deputy Inspector Hawkins replied. 'We have learned that a photographic crew of the Wild West Beanos advertising agency, Sydney Prescott & Associates, visited your crazy Uncle Hiram at the old T Bar X.'

'What the hell would an advertising agency be doing

105

at the old T Bar X?' Ida-Sue enquired, not unreasonably.

'We haven't got that quite nailed down yet, Mrs Jones,' Hawkins replied. 'But we're working on it. The only thing we know for sure is that the Sydney Prescott & Associates mobile photographic team was at the old T Bar X.'

'How can you be sure of that?'

'They don't get too many lavender Winnebagos in that part of Texas, ma'am,' Inspector Hawkins said. 'When they do get one, one with a Pansy Power! bumper sticker, they remember it.'

Ida-Sue looked thoughtful a moment.

'And where is this Sydney Prescott & Associates outfit, Hawkins?'

'In New York City, ma'am,' Hawkins replied. 'Where else?'

'Quite,' Ida-Sue said. 'Alamo, get off your rear end and get on the horn to the air force.'

'Certainly,' the congressman replied. 'What do you want me to tell the air force, Ida-Sue?'

'Tell them you have just learned of a serious threat to the nation's well-being and future security that requires you to be in New York City, together with your wife and a member of your staff, just as soon as an air force Sabreliner can get us there.

'I'll do that,' the congressman said. 'What's the threat, Ida-Sue, if you don't mind my asking? And which member of my staff?'

'The threat, Dummy, is that if it gets out that my daughter or your crazy Uncle or, God forbid, both of them, are running around with a crew of New York weirdos in a lavender Winnebago with a Pansy Power! bumper sticker on it, I'll never get to be First Lady of this great land of ours.'

'Right you are, Ida-Sue,' Alamo replied. 'And the member of my staff?'

'Raise your right hand, Dawkins,' Ida-Sue said. 'You are about to enter the service of the United States Congress.'

'That's Hawkins, ma'am,' he said.

'The first thing you're going to have to learn, Perkins, is that you don't argue with me. I'm a congressman's wife, and we're never wrong. Try to keep that in mind.'

And so it came to pass that when Sydney Prescott got off the Boston-New York shuttle and taxied to her offices high above Park Avenue, she found Lance Fairbanks (born Elroy Finley,) her chief of photographic services, rather beside himself with excitement.

'Sydney,' he greeted her, waving his yellow silk hankie excitedly. 'You'll never guess in a million years who's waiting for you in your office!'

'OK, I give up,' Sydney said. 'A word of warning, Elroy . . .'

'*Lance*, please!'

'Lance,' she corrected herself. 'Momma's had a trying day, Lance, and I'm in no mood to look at another of your models, no matter how handsome he is.'

'Nothing like that!' Lance said. 'We have a Congressman, that's who!'

'Whoopee!' Sydney said. 'Tell him I gave at the office and get rid of him.'

'And you'll never guess what he's going to do to you,' Lance went on.

'If he's like the rest of Congress, I can make one hell of a guess,' Sydney said, and pushed open the door to her office. The glower on her face turned to an instant smile when she saw the Honourable Alamo Jones. Whatever else could be said about Ms Prescott, she knew a good-looking man when she saw one, and Alamo Jones was physically a prime example of his gender, if beginning to show a bulge in the middle and the first hint of thinness on top.

'I am Sydney Prescott,' she announced dramatically. 'And to what can I attribute this unexpected pleasure?'

'Howdy, ma'am,' Alamo Jones said. 'The Honourable Alamo Jones at your service, ma'am.'

'Oh, I do hope so!' Sydney said.

'And I am Ida-Sue, Mrs Alamo Jones,' Ida-Sue said.

107

'I was afraid it would turn out to be something like that,' Sydney Prescott said. 'Well, let's get right to it. I'm a busy woman.'

'We have reason to believe that you have knowledge of our daughter,' Ida-Sue said. 'Where is she?'

'I haven't the foggiest idea what you're talking about,' Sydney Prescott replied, quite truthfully.

'And/or,' Ida-Sue went on, 'of my poor crazy Uncle Hiram.'

'Never heard of him, either,' Sydney said.

'And I suppose you never heard of Wild West Beanos, either?' Ida-Sue went on, thickly sarcastic.

'*Au contraire*,' Sydney said. 'That means, "Oh, yes, I do." Wild West Beanos are another of my brilliant thoughts, advertising-wise. One might say, indeed, that I am the mother of Wild West Beanos.'

'Aha!' Ida-Sue said, triumphantly. 'Then you admit it!'

'Admit what?'

'That you were at the old T Bar X,' Ida-Sue went on. 'In a lavender Winnebago with a Fruit Power! bumper sticker.'

'I believe that was Pansy Power! Ida-Sue,' Alamo Dave said.

'Shut up, Alamo,' Ida-Sue replied.

'I think you might be making reference to my chief of photographic services, Lance Fairbanks,' Sydney Prescott replied. 'He has a van that fits that description. And your handsome husband was right, as I'm sure he nearly always is. The bumper sticker does read Pansy Power!'

'See there, Ida-Sue?' Alamo Dave said.

'I told you to shut up, Alamo,' Ida-Sue said. 'OK, Ms Prescott, where is my daughter and/or my poor crazy Uncle Hiram?'

'Apparently, madame, you have never heard of advertising privilege,' Sydney Prescott said. 'While I'm not saying, one way or the other, whether I have any knowledge of your daughter and/or your poor crazy uncle, if

I did, hypothetically speaking, wild horses couldn't drag it from me.'

'How would you like to be presidential press secretary?' Ida-Sue responded.

'How would I like to be what?'

'You heard me. Presidential press secretary, in the glorious tradition of Ron Nesson, and that Baptist Preacher, whose name at the moment escapes me, but who served the *previous* president from Texas so well?'

'You're trying to suggest that your husband is going to seek the highest office in the land.'

'That's exactly what I'm suggesting,' Ida-Sue said.

'You've got my vote, Handsome,' Sydney said.

'Mine, too,' Lance Fairbanks said. 'And I've got just oodles of friends!'

'I shall try to be worthy of your trust and confidence,' Alamo said.

'Shut up, Alamo,' Ida-Sue said.

'And what does all this have to do with your daughter and your poor crazy uncle and me?' Sydney Prescott said.

'We have reliable information that you know something of their whereabouts,' Ida-Sue said.

'You mean to say you've lost them?' Sydney asked.

'Certainly someone in your profession can understand how important my husband's image is,' Ida-Sue said.

'I don't have to take that!' Sydney Prescott snapped. Then, more softly, 'Oh, you mean the *advertising* profession. How *foolish* of me! Yes, of course. But, professionally speaking, I'd say your husband has a very nice image, indeed.'

'Then you can appreciate the damage it would do to his ambitions, and to your own, presuming you would like to go down in the history books as the first female presidential press secretary, if it came out that Alamo's daughter had run off with a parachute freak, and that his Uncle Hiram had run off with a religious nut?'

Realization began to dawn.

'Tell me more about the parachute freak,' Sydney Prescott said.

'All I know is that my baby, Scarlett Rose-Marie, was last seen taking parachute instruction from a Green Beret HALO technician named Bubba. Now, what kind of behaviour is that for a University of Texas Marching Band Pompon Girl, I ask you?'

'A *former* UTMBPG, Ida-Sue, to be precise,' Alamo Jones said.

'Shut up, Alamo! She didn't mean it, she couldn't have meant it, when she said she was turning in her pompons. After all, it's a family tradition.' She turned to Sydney Prescott and explained. 'I'm a former UTMBPG myself, you know. They still talk about my *rah-rah-rahs* and my splits.'

'I'll bet they do,' Sydney said. 'In your opinion, Ida-Sue . . .'

'Mrs Jones to you, if you please!'

'In your opinion, is this parachute freak just a passing fancy, or is your daughter contemplating marriage . . . or even a somewhat less formal arrangement *à deux*?'

'Oh, my god!' Ida-Sue said. 'I don't know why I didn't think of that. That explains everything. Scarlett's parachute freak is after her money! He's nothing but an airborne gold digger!'

'I think I just may be able to help you,' Sydney Prescott said. 'And keep your daughter from marrying this gold-digger parachuter. It will be expensive, money-wise, however.'

'Cost be damned!' Ida-Sue said. 'You just get my Scarlett back to waving the pompons and send me your bill.'

'Now tell me about your poor crazy uncle,' Sydney Prescott said.

'He's in his fifties,' Ida-Sue replied. 'But it's hard to tell, because he has hair to his shoulders and a dirty grey beard to his belly button.'

'Ida-Sue, I thought you said the last time you saw him,

he was wearing a derby, carrying an umbrella, clean-shaven, and dressed like an Englishman,' Alamo said.

'I was obviously beside myself with anxiety,' Ida-Sue said. 'If you think about it, Uncle Hiram in a neck-tie, much less a suit, and not to mention a derby hat, staggers the imagination.'

'You're right, of course,' Alamo said.

'I'm always right, dear, you just keep forgetting that,' Ida-Sue went on. 'He is supposed to be in the company of a religious nut called the Reverend Mother Emeritus.'

'Got it,' Sydney Prescott said.

'And he's probably got Sitting Buffalo, his faithful Indian companion, with him,' Ida-Sue went on. 'So what you have to look for is a dirty bearded old man, a dirty old Indian, and a female religious nut. That shouldn't be hard to find.'

'I'll get right on it,' Sydney Prescott said. 'Just the moment I cash your cheque for my expenses.'

Chapter Ten

'It is so good of you, Mr Framingham,' Josephine Babcock cooed, extending her hand, 'to tear yourself from your busy schedule to help me with my problem.'

'Nonsense, dear lady,' Matthew Q. Framingham VI said, bowing and kissing her hand. 'The Framingham Foundation stands ever willing to assist in whatever manner possible any widow, not to mention the widow of a Framingham Foundation Fellow!'

'May he rest in peace,' Josephine said.

'I was afraid for a moment that I had the wrong VIP lounge,' Matthew said. 'A rather odd-appearing female came out of this room just now. Did you see her?'

'I believe she was here to clean the ashtrays,' Mrs Babcock replied.

'That's odd,' Matthew said. 'She asked me where she could catch the New York shuttle.'

'To get to the point, Mr Framingham,' Mrs Babcock said.

'I have engaged the Ambassadorial Suite at the Ritz-Carlton for our meeting, Widow Babcock,' Matthew said. 'I thought perhaps you might be good enough to partake of a small luncheon with me while we discuss the problem of your son.'

'I am a little hungry,' Josephine confessed. 'Although I had hoped we could go to meet Dr Pierce and Dr McIntyre immediately.'

'Haste makes waste!' Matthew said, solemnly.

'If I could only convince my Precious Babykins of that

profound truth!' Mrs Babcock said, as Matthew led her out of the VIP waiting room and into the Framingham Foundation's Rolls-Royce.

'A lovely motor-car,' Josephine Babcock said, as the Rolls rolled from Logan International Airport to the Ritz-Carlton.

'Do you really think so?' Matthew asked, visibly surprised.

'You don't think so?' she asked.

'If I may speak in confidence, Mrs Babcock,' Matthew said, 'frankly, no.'

'You don't like a Rolls-Royce?'

'The housekeeper is supposed to use the Rolls-Royce,' Matthew said. 'But when I went to the garage to pick up the Cadillac – we have a 1967 Cadillac – she had, against my express orders to the contrary, taken it to the A&P, leaving this thing for me.'

'But why should she do something like that?'

'She said that she simply cannot stand being laughed at in the A&P parking lot when, for example, she can't get the trunk open, or when the fool thing simply refuses to run. Be that as it may, she had no right to take the good car when I, in my official capacity as executive secretary of the Framingham Foundation, required safe and reliable transportation. I shall speak with her harshly at the first opportunity.'

'Isn't that odd?' Josephine said. 'I have the same trouble with mine.'

'You have a Rolls?'

'Three, actually,' Josephine said. 'I've found that's the only way I can be reasonably sure one will be working when I need one.'

'Good thinking!' Matthew said. 'Actually, lest you get the wrong idea, Widow Babcock – that is, that we toss money around at the Framingham Foundation – this one was a gift.'

'Oh, really?'

'A rather amusing story, actually,' Matthew said. 'Mr

Justice Canady . . . you know him, of course? Formerly of the Massachusetts Supreme Court?'

'By reputation,' Josephine said

'A Framingham Foundation Fellow, like your late husband,' Matthew went on.

'May he rest in peace,' Josephine said.

'Well, Mr Canady happened to be in Las Vegas, on Foundation Business,' Matthew said, 'together with myself, and Mr Fritz W. Fenstermacher, FFF.'

'As was my beloved late husband,' Josephine said.

'May he rest in peace,' Matthew said. 'Well, making her little joke, just prior to his departure from Boston, Mrs Justice Canady said, "Now, dear, don't you gamble away our life's savings on the crap tables while you are in Las Vegas."

'The Judge, as we call him, assured Mrs Canady that gambling was the furthest thing from his mind. It was duty to the Framingham Foundation that called him to Las Vegas.'

'The Mr Fritz W. Fenstermacher to whom you refer,' Josephine enquired. 'Is he the Fritz W. Fenstermacher, who is chairman of the board of Fenstermacher Breweries?'

'Indeed,' Matthew said.

'I've had the pleasure of meeting him,' Josephine said. 'At the last meeting of the Chairmen and Chairpersons of the Board Association.'

'It's a small world, isn't it?' Matthew offered, philosophically. 'Well, as I was saying, our business* in Las Vegas was accomplished in a shorter period of time than we had anticipated.'

'Nose to the grindstone,' Josephine replied. 'That sort of thing?'

'Quite,' Matthew said. 'And so Mr Justice Canady,

* The 'business' to which Mr Framingham referred here, and which has no relationship whatever to business as in 'financial business' or 'wholesale business' or the like, has been detailed at some length, for the insatiably curious, in M*A*S*H Goes to Las Vegas (Sphere Books, London).

with an idle moment to while away, dropped a quarter in one of those machines with the handle and the little windows with oranges and lemons . . .'

'I believe they're called slot machines,' Josephine offered helpfully.

'I believe they are. Well, he won. That is to say, he invested a quarter and the machine gave him back, if memory serves, $16.75.'

'How fortunate for him,' Josephine said.

'Well, being not only opposed to gambling in any form . . . which is a tenet of Framingham Theosophical Foundation, you know . . .'

'So I have been informed,' Josephine said, 'by my late husband, may he rest in peace, of course.'

'Well, then, you see Mr Justice Canady's problem. All he had wanted to do was to see the little oranges and lemons in the windows, and now he had $16.75, which he was forced to consider ill-gotten gambling gains.'

'I see his problem,' Josephine said.

'So he immediately began to reinsert quarters into the machine, in an attempt to get them back in, don't you see.'

'That seems to have been the thing to do under the circumstances,' Josephine said. 'And did he succeed?'

'The machine was apparently out of order, for every other time he put a quarter in the slot and pulled the handle, it gave him back another $16.75. Within a matter of minutes, he had a hat full of quarters.'

'How dreadful for him!'

'Well, one of the employees came over and confirmed that the machine was malfunctioning. He hung an out-of-order sign on it. The Judge asked what he should do with his ill-gotten gambling gains, and was directed to the cashier's window. He gave them the hat full of quarters. They insisted he take, in return, a stack of little round things bearing the logotype of the establishment.'

'Chips, I believe they are called,' Josephine said.

'I believe so,' Matthew went on. 'Well, Mr Justice

Canady didn't know what to do with them. He couldn't take them home, he realized, as a souvenir, for that would require answering the questions Mrs Canady would naturally ask regarding how he had come by them.'

'I understand,' Josephine said. 'So what did he do?'

'As he walked back towards the lobby, he passed a table. In the reasonable presumption that it had been placed there by some worthy charity, he discreetly laid the stack of chips on the table, and walked on towards the lobby.'

'Good thinking on his part,' Josephine said.

'Before he reached the lobby, however, he was intercepted by an employee of the establishment with the somewhat incoherent announcement that double zero had won, and what did he want done with his chips. He replied, of course, that he wanted nothing done with the chips, and again resumed his walk towards the lobby.

'And again, the employee intercepted him and told him that double zero had won again, and this time he would have to do something with his chips, for he had somehow exceeded something called the table limit.

' "But what am I to do with the chips?" he enquired.

'At that point, a third party entered the conversation. A Mr Porky Pig, leader of a musical ensemble known as Porky Pig and the Swine that had a professional engagement at the hotel, and who announced that he had had a little bad luck, and was consequently willing to exchange his automobile for the Judge's chips.

'Mr Justice Canady has always taken an interest in youth, even barefoot bearded youth in eye shadow and, simply to assist this young chap, turned over the chips to him. He then put the matter from his mind.

'Two weeks later, after we had returned to Massachusetts, an employee of Mr Pig delivered the automobile, this very Rolls-Royce, to Mr Justice Canady's home, saying both that Mr Pig was a man of his word, and that he had had one hell of a time finding the Judge. He left the car, so to speak, as a motherless foundling on

116

the Judge's doorstep. Since the Judge not only had a perfectly satisfactory automobile, a 1939 Packard, he had no need for an additional car, and turned it over to the Framingham Foundation. I've thought of selling it, of course, but I'm afraid that would be bad form. One doesn't sell gifts, does one?'

'Of course not,' Josephine agreed. 'And I must say that I admire you for holding to your standards of gentlemanly behaviour, Mr Framingham. I can see what a burden it has been for you.'

'Very kind of you to say so,' Matthew said. 'Oh, here we are.'

The Rolls rolled to a stop before the Ritz-Carlton. The doorman bowed as he reached to pull open the door. It wouldn't open. He tugged a little harder, and it still wouldn't open. Finally, with Matthew kicking from the inside while the doorman and two bellboys tugged from the outside, they got it open.

'Good afternoon, Mr Framingham,' the doorman said. 'Madame.'

'Good afternoon, Charles,' Framingham replied. 'I trust we are expected?'

'Indeed, sir,' the doorman said.

Josephine Babcock was absolutely sure that the doorman had winked at Matthew Q. Framingham.

An assistant manager, carnation in the buttonhole of his morning coat, greeted them just inside the door.

'How nice to have you with us, Mr Framingham,' he said. 'And you, too, madame.' He bowed them towards the elevator.

Josephine Babcock was absolutely sure that the assistant manager had also winked at Matthew Q. Framingham VI. And so, she saw, did the elevator operator as he slid the door shut.

'Might I ask you a personal question, Mr Framingham?' Josephine asked as they rose sedately upward.

'Of course,' Matthew replied.

'Do you come here often?'

117

'From time to time,' he said. 'But that's not a very personal question.'

The door to the elevator opened, temporarily suspending their conversation. The Ambassadorial Suite had been laid for lunch. There was a dining table covered with a heavy cloth, laden with glistening silver and shining crystal. There was a small candelabra, and a jeroboam of Piper Hiedseck cooling in a silver cooler. A recording of a gypsy violinist at his most romantic was coming softly over loudspeakers.

A waiter winked at Matthew Q. Framingham, and then left them alone.

'Might I offer you a glass of champagne, Widow Babcock, before we get down to business?'

'If you don't mind, Mr Framingham,' Josephine Babcock said. 'I think I'd rather have a martini. Light on the vermouth, please, and a double if you don't mind.'

'My pleasure,' Matthew replied, and with the speed and skill that comes only to martini mixers of long experience and those who keep in practice, he mixed up a batch, poured her one and took one for himself.

Josephine, the widow Babcock, was staring at him with undisguised curiosity. He was unnerved.

'Mr Framingham,' she said, 'you did bring me up here to discuss disengaging my son from that gold digger, didn't you?'

He flushed in the face, and it was a moment before he replied: 'I was afraid you'd notice,' he said. 'But believe me, Widow Babcock, I'm as embarrassed by this as you are. I can't imagine what these hotel people have been thinking *vis-à-vis* you and I.'

'I can,' Josephine said. 'And actually, I'm rather flattered,' she said. 'Not, I hasten to add, because there is any chance that I could be unfaithful to the memory of my late husband . . .'

'May he rest in peace,' Matthew said.

'But because it presents a possible solution to our little gold-digger problem.'

'And how is that?' Matthew enquired. 'Can I freshen your martini?'

'Don't mind if you do,' Josephine said. 'What I'm saying, Mr Framingham, is that it just occurred to me that the best way to deal with a gold digger is to feed her gold, or at least the appearance of gold.'

'I don't quite understand.'

'How old are you, Matthew?'

'Twenty-six.'

'Now, just between you and me, Matthew, while you're not nearly as handsome as my Precious Babykins, you're young enough for this big-busted blonde hussy, and with the Rolls and the clothing you're wearing, you look like you've got money.'

'I'm beginning, I think, to detect the direction of your thought,' Matthew said. 'Big-busted blonde, you said?'

'I have her photograph right here,' she said, taking one from her purse.

Matthew examined it with interest.

'Could you possibly find it in your heart, Mr Framingham, as a Framingham Foundation Fellow coming to the assistance of a poor widow woman, to make a pass at that big-boobed blonde gold digger?'

'Could I ever!' Matthew said. 'Let's drink to it!'

'Once Precious Babykins sees her for what she is,' Josephine said, holding out her own glass, 'this ridiculous notion of marriage will disappear.'

'You are a woman wise beyond your years, Widow Babcock,' Matthew said. 'It is a great honour for me to be able to come to your assistance in this matter, a great privilege to stand in, so to speak, for your late husband . . .'

'May he rest in peace . . .'

'. . . and rescue your innocent son from the clutches of this female. My, they are large, aren't they? And she obviously has no trouble passing the pencil test, either.'

'Give me the photograph back, please, Mr Framingham,'

Josephine said. 'Your hands are getting all sweaty.'

'Well now,' he said. 'Now that's all settled, shall we have another little nip before partaking of lunch?'

'You're a man after my own heart, Matthew,' she said. He turned to the bar and mixed another batch of martinis.

'I'm going to get on the telephone and see if I can find out where they are,' Josephine said. 'I presume you are free to accompany me?'

'Anywhere in the wide world, dear lady, in pursuit of this noble objective,' Matthew replied. 'I'd follow those . . . I mean, them . . . anywhere.'

Mrs Babcock had to make four telephone calls before she finally got word of the present whereabouts of Precious Babykins and the big-busted blonde hussy. Bubba had apparently tired of jumping Scarlett over Fort Bragg, and had carried her to Winston-Salem, where they had jumped in on his grandparents. Josephine's father had infuriated her by reporting that he found Scarlett charming, and by offering the opinion that Bubba 'was really a chip off the blockhead, blonde-wise, wasn't he?' He also reported that Bubba and Scarlett had left Winston-Salem aboard Bubba's plane, bound for Spruce Harbor, Maine, where they planned to jump in on two doctors whom they had met at the time they had met each other. En route, they planned to drop off three tons of dehydrated *soja hispida Babcockisis* at the old T Bar X, so that Bubba's plan to feed Uncle Hiram's *bison Americanus* could be put to the test.

'Let's go, Framingham,' Josephine had said, hanging up the phone. 'My Precious Babykins and that gold digger are on their way to Spruce Harbor.'

'Haste, my dear lady, as you yourself have pointed out, makes waste,' Matthew replied, handing her another martini. 'I suggest that having a quiet drink and a leisurely lunch will not only do wonders for our stomachs, but permit us to plan in great detail precisely how I am to woo Scarlett away from your Bubba.'

120

'You may have a point,' Josephine agreed. 'It can't be far away by jet, anyway.'

'Well, that's the sort of thing I mean. If I appear on *your* jet, that wouldn't get to Scarlett's gold-digger's heart nearly as much as arriving in my Rolls, now would it?'

'You're right, of course,' Josephine said.

Two hours later, Mr Matthew Q. Framingham VI and Mrs Burton Babcock III descended, somewhat unsteadily, the steps of the Ritz-Carlton, and stood there holding each other up, while the doorman, two bellboys and the assistant manager struggled to get the rear door of the Rolls open for them.

Then, their voices joined not unpleasantly in song, the two set out for Spruce Harbor, Maine, equipped, courtesy of the management, with a half-gallon pitcher of martinis against the rigours of the journey.

Chapter Eleven

At just about the time Chairperson and Presidentress Babcock and Executive Secretary Framingham settled down to partake of their first Oyster Onassis* in the Ambassador Suite of the Ritz-Carlton, a helicopter fluttered to the ground just over the hill from the simple ranch house of the old T Bar X.

A bald man with bad teeth and thick eyeglasses peered out the door and spoke to Taylor P. Jambon, who was in the process of unfastening his seat belt.

'You'd better be right about this, Jambon,' the bald man said. 'I'm beginning to have second thoughts about the whole thing.'

His voice was pleasant. It had resonance, depth, and machismo. It was, in fact, one of the most famous voices in America. It belonged to Don Rhotten, co-anchorperson of 'Waldo Maldemer & the Evening News Starring Don Rhotten,' which was telecast every evening at six PM to 11,456,567 viewing families.

'Have I ever led you astray, Don Baby?' Taylor P. Jambon replied.

'You bet your sweet blap you have!' Mr Rhotten replied.

'Aside from Vienna, I mean, Don Baby,' Jambon corrected himself, 'and that hurt me more than it hurt you, remember!'

'All that happened to you, Jambon, was that you were

---

* Lightly broiled in a sauce of garlic, truffles and champagne, and in sterling-silver ramekins, of course, in lieu of those ugly things in which oysters come, *au naturel*.

publicly revealed as a cheat and a scoundrel,' Don Rhotten said. '*I* was the one who got thrown in the fountain in full view of my 11,456,567 viewing families at home!'

'The water wasn't very deep in the fountain, Don,' Taylor said. 'You really didn't have to scream for help that way. You could have crawled out by yourself.'

'I've made up my mind,' Don Rhotten said. 'Coming here was a mistake!' He stuck his head out the door further and screamed up at the pilot: 'OK, Jack, back to civilization!'

'Now, wait a minute, Don,' Taylor P. Jambon said. 'You've come this far, you might as well take advantage of it.'

'Take advantage of what?'

'Of being out here in the wide-open spaces,' Taylor P. Jambon said. 'In your safari suit.'

'Get to the point, Jambon,' Don Rhotten said.

'All I'm suggesting, Don, is since you've come all this way you might as well have them shoot a little stock footage. You getting out of the helicopter, for example. And then standing there, looking philosophical, staring off over the plains.'

'I have your absolute guarantee there's no lions, tigers or anything else like that out there, right?'

'Would Taylor P. Jambon lie to you, Don Baby?'

'Do I have your guarantee – which means you get out first, and never get between me and the helicopter – or don't I?'

'You got it, Don,' Taylor P. Jambon said, extending his hand to be shaken.

'You know I don't like to shake your bare hand, Taylor,' Don Rhotten said. 'Either put a glove over that clammy skin of yours, or forget it!'

Mr Jambon cupped his hands over his mouth and yelled into the rear of the helicopter: 'Make-up! Camera crew! Audio!'

A group of technicians, a rather odd-appearing group

anywhere but here on the plains a sight to send the Chiricahua Apache fleeing in abject terror, disembarked from the ABS helicopter. The audio crew set up their microphones and mixers; the camera crew set up their cameras and lights and reflectors. And then the two crews, working together, set up a canvas fly under which, shaded from the sun, they could nap or play pinochle or otherwise idle away the time while the make-up crew, which had a far more difficult job, went to work on Mr Rhotten.

In the early days of his career, it had been a simple matter of simply sticking the Paul Newman-blue contact lenses in his eyes; installing the set of pearly white caps over his greyish, somewhat uneven teeth, and finally slapping the midnight black toupee with the boyish bangs on his head. But, with the passing of time, other problems had arisen. There were crow's feet at his eyes now, his jowls had begun to sag and he was lately the possessor of a purplish-red nose that would have put the proboscis of W. C. Fields to shame.

Treating these facial characteristics obviously took both time and skill, and more than an hour passed before Don Rhotten was ready to face the cameras.

When the day had dawned, Mr Rhotten had had absolutely no inkling that when the sun began to set, it would set on him in the wilds of west Texas. As a matter of fact, when the phone (his private unlisted number) had rung that morning, and he had seen how dark it was, he was afraid that he had overslept and it would again be time for him to be rushed by limousine to the ABS studios for the 'Evening News'.

'I hate to wake you up,' the familiar voice of Taylor P. Jambon had said. 'But this is important.'

'It's all right, Taylor,' Don Rhotten had replied graciously. 'It must be five o'clock anyway, and time for me to get to the studio.'

'It's six-fifteen, Don,' Jambon said.

'My god! I've missed the broadcast!'

124

'In the morning, Don,' Jambon said.

Mr Rhotten was now fully awake; the old brain, as he thought of it, was now firing on all four cylinders.

'What's the matter with you, Taylor? You been at the sauce again? You in your second childhood, or what? Sending me that box of stinky soap flakes – Jesus, what a smell! – was bad enough. But waking me up in the middle of the night! That's going too far, Jambon!'

'Those weren't soap flakes, Don,' Jambon replied.

'They looked like soap flakes,' Mr Rhotten replied. 'But when I soaked my tee shirts and boxer shorts in them, there was nothing left but the rubber bands and the labels.'

'Those weren't soap flakes, Don. That stuff is dehydrated *soja hispida Babcockisis.*'

'What?'

'The stuff I was telling you about. The stuff Burton Babcock & Company tried to feed my precious porkers.'

'You didn't have to send it to me, Jambon. I'll never get the smell out of here. And so far as I'm concerned you owe me three tee shirts and three boxer shorts. They were those Burt Reynolds Briefs, too, the sexy ones, with the slit on the side. Two ninety-eight a pair, I paid for them. That comes to . . . let me figure a moment . . .'

'I'll send you a cheque, Don.'

'You'd better.'

'I *wanted* you to smell it, Don,' Jambon said. 'That's why I sent it to you.'

'What are you, some kind of a smell freak? That was a lousy thing to do to a friend, Jambon.'

'I wanted you to see for yourself how horrible that stuff is.'

'You made your point.'

'I wanted you to see just how unspeakably cruel and barbaric Burton Babcock & Company is being to the poor animals.'

'You mean, they actually did try to feed that stuff to animals?'

'Yes, they did.'

'But you told me that pigs wouldn't eat it.'

'They wouldn't,' Jambon said. 'But now they've gone even further.'

'What the hell are you talking about?'

'I have it from a usually reliable, highly placed, confidential source,* Don, that Burton Babcock & Company, in a callous gesture of contempt not only for animal life but for one of America's most treasured symbols, is now going to try to feed it to buffaloes.'

'Buffaloes?'

'*Bison Americanus*,' Taylor said.

'I thought you said buffaloes.'

'I did.'

'I thought buffaloes were extinct,' Don Rhotten said.

'Not at all,' Taylor P. Jambon said.

'Jees, I didn't know that!'

'And those people at Burton Babcock & Company are going to try to feed them that stuff.'

'That's terrible, Taylor!' Don Rhotten said. 'Let's tell on them!'

'I thought you'd feel that way, Don.'

'Call the cops or something,' Don Rhotten said. 'There should be a law!'

'Indeed there should, and after the broadcast you're going to make, it will be known in the public's mind as the Don Rhotten Buffalo Protective Act.'

'What broadcast?'

'The one in which you bring this outrageous behaviour of Burton Babcock & Company to your 11,456,567 viewing families.'

'I'm going to do that?'

'Yes, you are.'

'You know I can't do that, Taylor,' Don Rhotten said. 'It would violate the television code.'

* He referred here, of course, to the pig thief, who was keeping an eye on the Possible Porcine Products Research Establishment from a tree house.

126

'No, it wouldn't,' Taylor P. Jambon said. 'The television code only prohibits saying nasty things about sponsors. They can't advertise cigarettes on the boob tube any more, Don. That means Burton Babcock & Company isn't a sponsor. You're free to say anything about them you want to.'

'You have a point, Jambon,' Mr Rhotten said. 'Sometimes you're not as dumb as you look. But how are we going to do it? We'd probably need special permission to bring a buffalo into New York City. Presuming we could catch one, I mean.'

'Well, Don, we're going to bring the mountain to Mohammad.'

'What the hell are you talking about now?'

'I mean, we're going out to where the buffalo roam, and the deer and the antelope play.'

'Where's that?'

'West Texas.'

'Like hell *we* are,' Don Rhotten said. 'You want *me* to do this show, *you* catch the buffalo and bring it here. In a sturdy cage.'

'Don, do you remember what you told me the last time I saw you?'

'The last time I saw you, you were so drunk they had to carry you out of P. J. Clarke's.'*

'Before that, I mean, when you opened your heart of hearts to me.'

'What about it?'

'You confessed that your greatest ambition in all the world was to join the staff of "One Hour".'

'So, I said that. So what?'

'And you told me that Harley Hazardous and Trenchcoat Wally Michaels had slipped it to you. I mean, in addition to having you thrown in the fountain.'

'Yes, they did,' Don Rhotten said. 'When I told them

---

* P. J. Clarke's is a New York City watering place popular with TV biggies. The decor has been described as early-New York Third Avenue.

I wanted to join "One Hour", they told me sure, just as soon as I dreamed up, and shot, a story on my own.'

'And what's happened?'

'I've shot six different stories on my own, and they won't show any of them,' Don Rhotten said. 'Good stories, too, like, "A Day in the Life of a Bagel Baker." Now, if that isn't a slice of life, what is?'

'You think they don't want you on the show, right?'

'That's what I think,' Don Rhotten said. 'They turned down the story I shot on Bella Abzug, too, the one I called, "Will Being Our First Female President Spoil Bella Abzug?"'

'You went a little far with that one, Don, when you said you had it on good authority that the Vatican was going to name her the first Jewish-American saint,' Taylor P. Jambon said. 'But the point I'm making is how could Harley Hazardous and Trenchcoat Wally Michaels turn down something called "Burton Babcock & Company Is Poisoning Our Buffaloes?"'

'You don't think they'd turn that down?'

'How could they? For one thing, it's true. And just to sweeten the old pot, Don, I wouldn't ever say that I gave you the idea. You can say that you found out about what was going on by yourself. You'd get all the credit.'

'Well, maybe, Taylor. But I still think you ought to bring the buffaloes to me, and we'll just poison them in the studio.'

'You told me you'd do anything to get on "One Hour",' Taylor said. 'Make any sacrifice, pay any price. That means going to Texas.'

'How long would I have to stay?'

'I got a jet laid on to take you from New York to Midland,' Taylor said. 'And a helicopter laid on in Midland. You wouldn't have to spend more than an hour or so actually in Texas. Just time enough for a couple of location shots, and maybe two minutes of the buffalo writhing in agony after we feed them this stuff.'

'Well, OK,' Don Rhotten said.

'Wear the safari suit, Don,' Taylor said. 'But leave the sun helmet home.'

'You know what happens to my head the minute I get in the sun,' Don Rhotten said. 'I blister easily, Taylor.'

'Wear your rug.'

'When I wear the rug in the sun, my head sweats and the rug slips.'

'We'll work something out,' Taylor said. 'I'll meet you in Midland, Don.'

When the ABS chartered jet arrived at the airport in Midland, Taylor P. Jambon had other details of the story worked out. The pig thief had reported that both Burton Babcock IV and Mrs Josephine Babcock had left Burton County. Mrs Babcock, in her jet, was going to Boston, and Burton Babcock IV was going to Maine, via Texas, after jumping his girl friend at Fort Bragg.

'I'd sort of hoped to catch them in the act, Don,' Taylor said. 'But what we'll have to do is just shoot the pieces of the story. Get some footage of the buffalo here, some footage of the boxes of this stuff, then get some footage of Mrs Babcock and her buffalo-poisoning son, and put it all together.'

'What are you going to do about the buffalo writhing in agony?'

'I got some stock footage of that in Hollywood. Out-takes from an old movie called *Buffalo Bill at the Battle of the Little Big Horn*. Then all we have to do is splice it all together.'

'Sure,' Don Rhotten said. 'Why not? We do that all the time.'

Finally, the make-up artists had Don Rhotten ready to face the cameras. The helicopter took off again, and then landed as the cameras turned. Wearing his familiar look of determination, Don Rhotten leapt out of the helicopter just before it touched down. He caught his toe in the landing skid and landed on all fours and said a dirty word, but that could be edited out. Then the cameras followed him as he walked over the rise to the run-down ranch house of the old T Bar X.

'Jees,' he said. 'Look at that hairy cow.'

'That's a buffalo, Don,' Taylor P. Jambon said.

'I don't think he likes me,' Don Rhotten said. 'Enough is enough.' He turned and ran back to the helicopter and nothing Taylor P. Jambon could do or say was sufficient to get him to leave again.

Jambon returned to the ranch house with the camera crew. He took up a position on the porch from which he could direct their efforts and one which, he felt reasonably sure, would keep the buffalo from attacking.

'Sneak up on that one lying down,' he ordered. 'And then make up a noise or sómething and get him to stand up. We can run the film backward with a voice-over saying he's just eaten some of this stuff.'

As they were doing that, his eyes naturally wandered around the premises. They fell upon what looked like a case of groceries. He walked over, ripped the carton open and came out with a can labelled Wild West Beanos. He had not, he told himself, become America's Most Famous TV Gourmet by being unwilling to taste test everything that came to his attention. (This also contributed to his girth, which he regarded as his badge of bravery, culinarily speaking.)

He took his Hammacher Schlemmer Gentleman's Handy Dandy Can Opener from his vest pocket, opened the can, and then sampled the contents with his sterling silver folding fork.

'Ummm,' he said. 'Goody!' He wondered how it was that someone of all his all-around expertise, food-wise, had not encountered this product before. He examined the can carefully. 'Packed by the BB&C Cannery,' it said. He had never heard of the BB&C Cannery, but it was as sure as the night follows day that, shortly after he extolled the virtues of this '100% Pure, 100% American Grown product to all his fans out there in TV Land, the BB&C Cannery would find some way in which to express their gratitude to him. Say with a nice little cheque plus, of course, a lifetime supply of Wild West Beanos.

'You, there!' Taylor P. Jambon called to one of the grips. 'When you finish waking that buffalo up, bring this case of my newly discovered gustatory goodie back with you to the helicopter.'

When he returned to the helicopter, Don Rhotten, looking somewhat ashen faced, was slumped in his seat, his rug in his lap, mopping at his head with a handkerchief.

'That was a harrowing experience!' he said. 'That beast wanted me for supper, I could tell by the look in his eyes.'

'Speaking of supper,' Taylor P. Jambon said, 'have a taste of this, Don. My latest discovery.'

'What is it?'

'Trust me, Don,' Taylor said. 'Before I'm through with it, it will be as American as Wheaties.'

Don Rhotten carefully wiped Taylor P. Jambon's sterling silver folding fork with the handkerchief he had been using on his head, and dipped in.

'Say,' he said. 'That's good!'

'It's like peanuts,' Taylor P. Jambon said. 'Once you start eating, you can't stop. Fortunately, I have a whole case.'

'What happens now?' Don Rhotten asked.

'We go to Boston,' Taylor P. Jambon said. 'Where you accost the chairperson and presidentress of Burton Babcock & Company personally, and demand to know, on behalf of the American people, how dare she poison America's buffaloes with her horrible *soja hispida Babcockisis.*'

'Serve her right,' Don Rhotten said, somewhat unclearly through a mouth stuffed with Wild West Beanos. 'Cancelling TV advertising is tantamount to treason against the American way.'

Chapter Twelve

Wrong Way Napolitano, proprietor of Spruce Harbor International Airfield, looked up from the well-thumbed copy of *Playboyo Italiano* with which he was whiling away his duty hours in the control tower to see a Learjet approaching from the sea at about 450 knots and no more than a hundred feet over the water.

He looked at it idly. It had been his experience that while an aircraft performing in that manner might be considered odd at other installations, it was not at all unusual at Spruce Harbor International. It was probably, he decided, either Col. Horsey de la Chevaux, making an unexpected visit in one of his airplanes, or an Air Hussid aircraft, bearing either His Royal Highness Sheikh Abdullah ben Abzug or Boris Alexandrovich Korsky-Rimsakov, the World's Greatest Opera Singer.

In just a second now, Wrong Way thought to himself rather professionally, the Learjet would pop the ol' speed brakes, drop the ol' gear, touch down, and hit the ol' reverse thrust lever. Then his eyes widened as it became evident that the Learjet was about to do none of these things. Without losing a mile of airspeed, and dropping down to about fifty feet of altitude, it did a barrel roll down the runway, pointed its nose skyward, and kicked in something Wrong Way had not been previously aware was an optional accessory from the friendly folks at Learjet, what he thought of as the ol' afterburner.

It soared practically straight up, giving off dense clouds of unburned fuel. Wrong Way grabbed for the red emergency telephone that connected the control tower directly with the Spruce Harbor Medical Centre switchboard.

'Now don't get excited, Hazel,' he said to Mrs Heidenheimer, in a piercing voice perhaps one-half decibel less loud than the sirens atop Spruce Harbor's shining red fire engines. 'But I think we're about to have an emergency down here at the airport!'

'An *emergency* emergency?' Hazel enquired. 'Or are you out of Chianti again?'

'You just tell Hawkeye and Trapper John I said they'd better get down here right away with an ambulance.' He slammed the phone down in the cradle and then, after glancing out the window, picked it up again. 'Make that two ambulances, Hazel, I see two chutes opening.'

There are those who point to the speed and enthusiasm with which Drs Trapper John McIntyre and Hawkeye Pierce respond to an emergency call as another manifestation of the seriousness with which they regard the Hippocratic oath and their sacred and solemn duty to offer aid and succour to their fellow man at the earliest possible moment. There are those, too, to be evenhanded about it, who believe that both healers are flashing-red-light-and-siren freaks, to whom the professional services rendered at the conclusion of the journey is a small-enough price to pay for having been permitted (even encouraged) by society generally, and the minions of the law specifically, to race down tranquil streets at excessive speeds, red lights flashing, sirens and whoopers screaming and whoop-whoop-whooping, the cynosure of all eyes, scattering all lesser beings from their path.

The proponents of this latter theory point to the facts that the two take turns at the wheel of the ambulance, that arguments about who will drive are a great source of disagreement between them, and that the nominal driver of the ambulance (to whom it is necessary to pay a hazardous duty bonus whenever either healers beats him to the wheel) often returns from riding in the back during a run in obvious need of medical tranquillization.

133

No one, least of all Wrong Way Napolitano, therefore, was in the least surprised when Spruce Harbor Medical Centre's Ambulance Number Three (whose mechanical needs were seen to, at the insistence or Drs Pierce and McIntyre, by the Rock Bound Coast Speed Shop, Hot Rod Emporium and Garage) arrived at Spruce Harbor International, setting a new record in the process, about thirty seconds before the two striped canopies deposited the escapees from the Learjet on terra firma.

'Not bad,' Wrong Way said to Dr Pierce, after consulting his stopwatch. 'Two minutes, forty and sixty-four one hundreths seconds. That's a new record, I think.'

'I knew it was going to be a good run,' Hawkeye Pierce replied. 'The roads were dry, and I was in good shape. But I'd like to express my appreciation to the fine mechanics at Rock Bound Coast SS, HRE and G,* without whom none of this would have been possible.'

'Touchdown!' John F. X. McIntyre, MD, FACS said, obviously trying to change the subject.

The larger of the two parachutists had indeed landed.

'Look!' Wrong Way said. 'He's going to break the fall of the other one by catching it with his own.'

'That's one way to look at it,' Hawkeye said.

'And whatever was wrong with the plane,' Wrong Way said, 'has apparently been corrected. Look, here it comes in for a landing.'

The two parachutists were now both on the ground, wrapped in what, even at that distance, was obviously a fond embrace.

'I wonder what they're doing?' Wrong Way asked.

'I think he's spreading pollen on her,' Trapper John said. He reached inside the ambulance and turned the siren on and off. The sound startled the parachutists, who broke apart, and then, holding hands, came gaily skipping down the grass beside the runway towards the ambulance.

* A.k.a. the Rock Bound Coast Speed Shop, Hot Rod Experts and Garage.

'Hello there, Doctors Pierce and McIntyre,' Bubba Babcock boomed in his deep voice, his pearly white teeth revealed in a wide smile. 'You remember the Little Lady, of course?'

'How'd you know we were coming?' Scarlett asked. 'We thought we would drop in on you as a little surprise.'

'We're here for the blood test,' Bubba announced. 'Under the circumstances, of course, the Little Lady and I wouldn't dream of having someone else do it.'

Scarlett blushed. 'We can't wait until we get married,' she said.

'I noticed,' Trapper John replied. 'But this is the Rock Bound Coast, and around here the law says you have to wait.'

The conversation was, fortuitously, interrupted at that point by the landing of Bubba's personal airplane.

'Colonel,' Bubba said to the jolly, bald-headed, barrel-chested pilot, Col. Merritt T. Charles, USA, retired, 'these gentlemen are Drs Pierce and McIntyre – Hawkeye and Trapper John to their legion of friends – who advised Scarlett and I to enter the state of wedded bliss.'

'What I did, actually,' Hawkeye corrected him, 'was to agree with you and that religious chap whose name unfortunately escapes me at the moment that it is indeed better to marry than to burn. At the time I said that, I think it germane to point out, the two of you were already smouldering.'

'No matter how you slice it, gentlemen,' Colonel Charles said, 'your you-know-whats are in a crack with Bubba's Mama for saying that.'

'So we have been led to believe,' Trapper John said. 'Colonel, you sound familiar. Have we met before?'

'I was just thinking the same thing,' Colonel Charles said. He paused thoughtfully. 'You weren't, by any chance, engaged in the Korean police action?'

'You could put it that way,' Trapper John said.

'The 4077th MASH!' Colonel Charles cried triumphantly. 'You're the two who encased Hot Lips' boy-friend in plaster of Paris.'

'Guilty,' Hawkeye said.

'And the ones who crucified the chaplain!' Colonel Charles said.

'It might have looked to some people that way,' Trapper John said. 'We really didn't intend to leave him tied to the cross longer than overnight.'

'Oh,' Colonel Charles said. 'I'm really sorry to hear that!'

'I gather you knew the reverend gentleman?' Hawkeye asked.

'Unfortunately,' Colonel Charles said. 'He took advantage of my condition.'

'What condition was that?'

'I had one broken leg and one broken arm,' Colonel Charles replied. 'Suffered in the service of our country when I fell off my junk.'

'I beg your pardon?' Scarlett asked.

'An Oriental-type seagoing vessel, Scarlett,' Colonel Charles said.

'I remember a guy with a broken arm and a broken leg who fell off his junk,' Trapper John said.

'I remember him, too,' Hawkeye said. 'But he was one of those natty young majors. It wasn't this guy. Our guy was trim, slim and had a full head of hair.'

'Thanks a lot!' Colonel Charles said.

'You were telling us that you knew "Swinging Sammy"?'* Trapper John said, hastily.

'There I was, up to my you-know-what in plaster of

---

* Dr McIntyre here referred to Rev. Samuel J. Abbott, now pastor of the Third Baptist Church of Ozark, Alabama, who once served (while a captain chaplain) as spiritual advisor to the 4077th MASH. He was retired medically from the service on a seventy-percent disability pension, having suffered what was described as severe mental and emotional trauma while at the 4077th MASH. The details are recorded in *M*A*S*H Goes to New Orleans* (Sphere Books, London).

Paris,' Colonel Charles said, 'when he spotted me. Talk about a captive audience! I'd probably be singing in a choir somewhere today if you guys hadn't crucified him.'

'We're glad that we were able to be of some small service to you, Colonel,' Hawkeye said.

'It was our pleasure,' Trapper John added.

'And Hot Lips!' Colonel Charles said, warmed by the memory. 'How often I've wondered about ol' Hot Lips! You guys don't happen to know whatever happened to her, do you? Now, there was a nurse!'

'I was afraid you'd ask,' Hawkeye said.

'She has, in a sense, taken to religion,' Trapper John said. 'Would you believe that it's the Reverend Mother Emeritus now, Colonel?'

'Swinging Sammy got to her?' the Colonel asked in disbelief.

'Not so far as I know,' Trapper John said.

'Spiritually, the colonel means,' Hawkeye said.

'Not that way, either,' Trapper John replied.

'Gee, I'd like to see her again!' Colonel Charles said, wistfully.

'I was afraid of that, too,' Hawkeye said. 'The Reverend Mother Emeritus seems to have that effect on people.'

'Are you talking about *our* Reverend Mother Emeritus?' Scarlett asked.

'I'm afraid so,' Hawkeye said.

'What do you mean, "our Reverend Mother Emeritus"?' Colonel Charles asked, somewhat confused.

'She's the one who got Uncle Hiram to take a bath,' Scarlett said. 'And the one who was going to marry us, until she remembered that Bubba's mother would like to be there.'

'I've been thinking about that, Little Lady,' Bubba said. 'It seems only fair that if my mother is at our joining together in the bonds of wedded bliss, your parents should also be there.'

'I realize that this makes me sound like a cold, cruel

and ungrateful daughter,' Scarlett said. 'But I have dreamed since I was a little girl of my wedding day, of walking down the aisle to be joined together, till death do us part, to my own beloved husband. I don't want that ruined by my father giving one of his speeches and my mother waving her damned pompons.'

'I beg your pardon?'

'I'd rather not talk about it any more, Dr McIntyre, if you don't mind.'

'Whatever you say, honey,' Dr McIntyre replied.

'I don't suppose there's some place in this quaint little village of yours where a man could get a drink, is there?' Colonel Charles enquired.

'By the wildest imaginable coincidence, Colonel,' Hawkeye said, 'there is. I propose that we adjourn to the Bide-a-While. We can make sleeping arrangements for the lovebirds while we're there.'

Scarlett flushed and squeezed Bubba's hand. Bubba tried to look nonchalant.

'Bubba goes to my house,' Trapper John said. 'And Scarlett to yours.'

The smiles on the lovebirds faded.

'You're a party pooper, McIntyre,' Hawkeye said, softly, to him. 'I've always said that.'

The Bide-a-While Pool Hall, Ladies Served, Fresh Clams & Lobsters Daily Restaurant & Saloon, Inc., Stanley K. Warczinski, Sr., owner & manager, drink Coca-Cola was widely known along the Rock Bound Coast not only because its sign was the largest sign ever erected by the good people of the Coca-Cola Company for an individual business,* and not only because the pile of empty beer cans and whiskey bottles behind it is the second largest east of the Mississippi, nor even for its reputation as the 'in' place among Spruce Harbor's

---

* The Coca-Cola representative had told Mr Warczinski that he could have the sign absolutely free of charge, and that he could advertise his business in any (non-obscene, of course) way he chose, just so long as it said Coca-Cola somewhere on it. The representative is no longer associated with the Coca-Cola Company.

motorboating set, but rather because, on occasion, departing from his usual glum and surly attitude, the proprietor will sometimes develop, at first sight, an instant affection for a new customer, and thereafter lavish unparalleled hospitality on him/her. While it is true that his mood strikes Mr Warczinski only after he has been imbibing a bit more than he should, this does not detract from the event for it is quite difficult, even for those who know him well, to detect the difference between Warczinski sober and Warczinski drunk.

On this occasion, Mr Warczinski (beneath whose massive, hairy chest there beat the heart of a romantic; his hero was Frederick Chopin) developed, the moment he saw the ease with which Bubba moved aside the two fifty-gallon beer kegs that barred the door in order to permit Scarlett to pass, an instant affection for the both of them.

'Despite those pearly white teeth and that massive chest,' Stanley said, moving with surprising grace for his bulk from the barstool on which he had been sitting and philosophizing to the door, 'there's mixed blood in you. But half a Pole is better than no Pole at all, as I always say. On the other hand, your lady friend, I can tell from the blonde hair and those boobs, is pure Pole!'

'Watch it, Stanley!' Hawkeye warned.

'I thought I'd seen the last of you,' Colonel Charles said. 'I'd hoped you were lost at sea!'

Stanley K. Warczinski looked at Colonel Charles for a moment with a look of bafflement, not unlike that of an elephant who has just ingested a bunch of plastic bananas, and then recognition dawned.

'Major Charles!' he said, and swept the colonel off his feet and kissed him wetly on each cheek. 'I haven't seen you since I threw you off the junk.'

'You were drunk then, too, as I recall. Set me down, you overstuffed Polack!'

'Threw him off the junk, you said, Stanley?' Trapper John enquired.

'The major said the next time he caught me making vodka on the junk's still, he'd throw the still over the side. I said if he threw the still over the side, I'd throw him over the side. He did and he did and I did. But there were no hard feelings.'

'The only reason I didn't shoot you when I got back from the hospital was because they told me you'd been lost at sea,' the colonel said.

'I was,' Stanley said. 'But the navy found me.'

'I've never liked the navy,' Colonel Charles said.

'This is one of the happiest moments of my life,' Stanley K. Warczinski said, as tears rolled down his sagging, unshaven cheeks. 'Reunited with my commanding officer, after all these years!'

'Not another crying drunk, Warczinski,' Colonel Charles pleaded. 'I couldn't stand that again.'

'Momma,' Stanley shouted to Mrs Warczinski. 'Bring in a couple of gallons of the good vodka!'

'It is a pleasure, sir,' Bubba said, 'to meet a fellow veteran.'

'Tell me all about you and this Polish beauty, son!' Stanley said.

'I'm not Polish,' Scarlett said.

'Nonsense,' Stanley said. 'Blood tells. But what's a nice Polish girl like you doing with Pierce, McIntyre and this bald-headed dirty old man?'

'Bubba and I are going to be married, Mr Warczinski,' Scarlett said.

'And I,' Stanley said, 'Stanley K. Warczinski, Sr., will provide the traditional Polish wedding feast! It's the least one Pole can do for another!'

'The wedding, Stanley,' Hawkeye said, 'won't take place just yet.'

'Not until tomorrow,' Scarlett said.

'Perhaps as late as tomorrow afternoon,' Bubba agreed.

The telephone rang. Stanley grabbed it, listened momentarily, said, 'He's not here,' and hung up. Then he turned to Hawkeye and announced, 'That was for you.'

'You didn't happen to catch who it was calling, did you?'

'It was the long-distance operator,' Stanley replied.

'Did she say, by any chance, who was calling and from where?'

'Esther Flanagan was calling from Montreal,' Stanley replied. At that moment, the telephone rang again.

'If that's for me, Stanley,' Hawkeye said, quickly, 'I'll take it.'

'Answer it yourself then,' Stanley snapped. 'Momma, where the hell is that vodka?'

Hawkeye took the telephone.

'The Bide-a-While,' he said.

'Hawkeye, Hazel,' Hazel Heidenheimer said. 'I thought you'd be there.'

'Well, you were right,' Hawkeye said. 'How much did you win?'

'There's a Rolls-Royce outside, Hawkeye,' Hazel said.

'A Rolls-Royce?'

'With two drunks in it.'

'I'm afraid to ask what a Rolls-Royce with two drunks in it has to do with me,' Hawkeye replied. 'But curiosity has got the better of me.'

'One of the drunks is that funny-talking big ape from Cambridge,' Hazel said.

'You are referring, Hazel, to Matthew Q. Framingham VI, executive secretary of the Framingham Theosophical Foundation?'

'You got it,' she said.

'And the lady?'

'I don't know. Both of them are out like a light. The chauffeur said that they came here to see you, that the lady met the big ape in Boston, at the airport.'

Hawkeye looked over his shoulder to see if Bubba was within earshot. When he saw that he was not, he went on: 'Hazel, get a couple of practical nurses, and unload the lady. Put her to bed in a private room, put a

141

COMPLETE REST, DO NOT DISTURB sign on the door. As a humanitarian gesture, you'd better put a couple of Alka-Seltzers on the bedside table, too.'

'Gotcha,' she said. 'And the big ape?'

'Send him over here,' Hawkeye said.

'What's this all about, Hawkeye?'

'I made a big mistake, Hazel,' Hawkeye confessed. 'I told the big ape to do whatever he thought was necessary to keep the lady off my back.'

'Who is she?' Hazel said.

'I wouldn't want this to get out, Hazel,' Hawkeye said, 'but she's somebody's mother.'

'I understand completely,' Hazel said. 'I'll take care of everything.'

Hawkeye still had his hand on the telephone, hanging it up, when it rang again.

'Bide-a-While,' he said.

'If you know what's good for you, you overstuffed Polish sausage, you'll get Hawkeye on the horn, and right now!'

'This is Dr Pierce,' Hawkeye replied. 'With whom do I have the pleasure of speaking, as if I didn't know?'

'Dr Pierce,' Esther Flanagan said, very shyly, 'this is Esther Flanagan.'

'How's things in Montreal?' Hawkeye enquired.

'Oh, things are just sublime!' Esther said.

'Sublime?'

'Sublime,' Esther confirmed. 'Dr Pierce, you are one of the best friends I have in the world,' Esther went on.

'Well, I'm happy if I am, but if I am, why don't you call me Hawkeye like you usually do?'

'I have a great favour to ask of you, one I wouldn't dare ask if I didn't regard you as my most respected friend,' Esther said.

'Name it,' Hawkeye said.

'Give me away,' Esther said.

'I beg your pardon?'

'Give me away to Henri Flambeau, I mean.'

'To who?'

'Henri Flambeau,' Esther repeated.

'I never heard of him,' Hawkeye said. 'And why should I give you to him?'

'In marriage, I mean,' Esther said. 'Henri has just asked me to be his bride.'

'Esther, not you, too!' Hawkeye said. 'One pair of overheated lovebirds is all I can handle at one time.'

'What did you say?'

'I said, how nice for you,' Hawkeye replied.

'Then you will?'

'Then I will what?'

'Give me away.'

'Marriage, Esther,' Hawkeye began, 'is not something to be entered into frivolously or lightly. And besides, what about Hiram?'

'Don't be silly, Hawkeye,' Esther said. 'Why should I marry a dirty old bearded buffalo rancher when a *gentleman*, one affiliated with the provincial government in a communications capacity, has asked me to become his blushing bride?'

'You may have a point,' Hawkeye said. 'But if you're asking for my advice, Esther, you'll consider this carefully, over a reasonable period of time.'

'I'm not asking your advice,' Esther, sounding like Esther normally sounded, snapped. 'Are you going to give me away or not?'

'Can I bring Trapper John with me, to give me courage?' he asked.

'Of course, you can,' she said. 'I want you and Trapper John to be friends with my Henri right from the beginning!'

'When, to coin a phrase, do you plan to tie the knot?'

'Just as soon as you get here,' she said. 'A man of Henri's influence, him being associated with the provincial government and all, can just cut through the red tape like a buzz saw through hot peanut butter.'

143

'Where are you, Esther?'

'I'm in the Jean Claude Killy Suite of the Vieux Montreal Howard Johnson's Motel,' she said. 'How soon can you get here?'

'We're on our way,' Hawkeye said.

Chapter Thirteen

'Now, see here, Sadie,'* Lance Fairbanks said, just as indignantly as he knew how, 'there are limits to the sacrifices I am willing to make for my profession. I've already been to Texas, and I still shudder to think of the crude and cruel things they said to Brucie and me down there. I have *no* intention of going to Maine.'

'Don't call me Sadie, Elroy,' Sydney said. 'I've told you that before.'

'A rose by whatever name, so to speak,' Lance said. 'I'm *not* going to Maine, and that's all there is to it! I think Bubba meant every word he said about the rule he had in the Green Berets that he brought home with him.'

'What rule are you talking about?' Sydney asked.

'He said they had a rule in the Green Berets that if someone like me or Brucie came within an imaginary six-foot circle around them, they broke their legs. And I just know in my heart that he meant it!'

'Well, then, all you have to do is keep your hands to yourself, Lance, and stay six feet away from him. I told you this was business, not pleasure.'

'Oh, phooey!' Lance said.

'You mean to tell me you don't want to become the official personal photographer to the President of the United States?' Sydney asked.

'What are you talking about?'

* Although it was one of the most closely guarded secrets of Sydney Prescott & Associates, it was whispered about that Ms Sydney Prescott had gone through the first twenty-one years of her life with the name given on her birth certificate, Sadie Krausnitz. Unlike most whispers, this one was right on the target.

'When I am presidential press secretary in the Alamo Jones administration,' Sydney said, 'I'll be in a position to put in a very good word for you, Lance, when the question of official personal photographer to the President comes up.'

'You don't mean to sit there with a straight face and tell me you think that brainless ex-football player, that smiling ex-farmboy, El Teetho, stands a chance to actually become President of the United States, do you?'

'Think about it, Lance,' Sydney said. 'Stranger things have happened, President-wise.'

'What exactly am I supposed to do in Maine?' Lance asked. 'I can see that my country is calling.'

'All we have to do is bust up this romance,' Sydney said. 'And it's 1600 Pennsylvania Avenue, here we come!' Sydney said. 'We'll think of something.'

'Can Brucie come along?' Lance asked. 'He gets so depressed when I leave him behind with nothing to do but water our rubber plant.'

'If you think it necessary,' Sydney said. She picked up the telephone and dialled a number.

'Around-the-World Travel Agency?' she said. 'Sydney Prescott of Sydney Prescott & Associates, calling personally. Let me speak with someone important.' There was a moment's delay, and then she said, 'I need three seats, two tourist and one first-class, on the very next flight to Spruce Harbor, Maine.' There was another pause, this time a rather longer one. 'What do you mean, there's no way to get there from here?' she exploded. Another pause. 'Well, if that's the way it has to be, that's the way it has to be. Damn the expense! Charter an airplane, and send the bill to the Honourable Alamo Jones, MC.'

They left the office of Sydney Prescott & Associates a few minutes later, bound, via a stop on Washington Mews to pick up Brucie, for John F. Kennedy International Airport to meet their chartered plane for the flight to the wilds of Maine.

They were not, however, as they naturally presumed, alone. Another taxi-cab, its driver urged to new heights of recklessness by Ida-Sue Jones, who fed him a steady stream of twenty-dollar bills, stayed right on their bumper.

In the second cab, as Lance sort of floated into the Washington Mews apartment to fetch Brucie, Ida-Sue turned to the congressman and said, 'You see, Stupid, I was right again.'

'You're always right, Ida-Sue,' the congressman agreed. 'I know that.'

'You keep forgetting it,' she said. 'I knew that horrible woman knew where my little Scarlett and/or poor crazy Uncle Hiram was.'

'Who would have thought it possible that my darling daughter and/or poor crazy Uncle Hiram would wind up in an apartment in a New York slum like this.'

'I don't think they're in there, Alamo, and this isn't a slum. This is a very select neighbourhood.'

'You're kidding!'

Lance, holding Brucie by the hand, came rushing back out of the apartment, shutting off any further conversation. With Ida-Sue and Alamo in close pursuit, they drove on to John F. Kennedy.

'Just think, Alamo,' Ida-Sue said, 'one day this airfield will be the Alamo Jones International Airport.'

'But it's already got a name,' he protested.

'And it had a name before they called it John F. Kennedy,' Ida-Sue replied. 'Fame passes, Alamo. The Kennedy family will just have to do what the Idlewild family did: take their lumps, step out of the spotlight, and realize that time marches on.'

'The Idlewild family?'

'That's what it was before it was Kennedy,' Ida-Sue said. 'He was vice-president under Millard G. Fillmore.'

Ida-Sue and Alamo watched as Sydney, Lance and Brucie boarded the chartered airplane and prepared to take off. Then they rushed across the field to where Air Force 909, the aircraft assigned to Congressman Jones by the grateful taxpayers for his travel in the public interest, sat waiting.

'Follow that airplane!' Ida-Sue cried, as she jumped aboard. She turned to speak to her husband, who was shaking hands with the man with the fire extinguisher. 'Get on the plane, Dummy!' she barked. 'Time's a-wasting!'

Meanwhile, back at the Bide-a-While, Dr Benjamin Franklin Pierce was in deep conversation with Dr John Francis Xavier McIntyre. They were huddled, *tête-à-tête*, at the end of the bar, between the gallon jar of pickled eggs and the pigs knuckles.

'Are you sure Esther is serious?' Trapper John asked. 'I thought she was just kidding about having a gentleman admirer.'

'She's serious,' Hawkeye replied. 'She even gave me his name. Henri Flambeau.'

'She's marrying the premier?' Trapper John asked. 'I thought he already had a wife!'

'The premier's not named Flambeau, Trapper. He's got another funny name. Budreau, I think.'

'Right!' Trapper John said. 'Then who is this Flambeau character?'

'He's connected with the provincial government in a communications capacity.'

'You could say the same thing about me,' Trapper John replied. 'I'm connected with the United States government in a communications capacity. The IRS sends me threatening letters, and I send them money.'

'You're suggesting that Flambeau may not be the right Mr Right for our Esther?'

'That possibility has passed through my mind,' Trapper John said.

'Well, what do we do?' Hawkeye asked. 'I told her we were coming right away.'

'We'll go, of course,' Trapper John said.

The telephone rang. As Hawkeye grabbed for it, he said, 'Cross your fingers, maybe it'll be Esther calling us back to tell us she was kidding.'

But it was not Esther, it was Wrong Way Napolitano.

'Bide-a-While,' Hawkeye said. 'Stanley's not here.'

'Hawkeye? Is that you? How come you're answering the phone?'

'I found out that when I pick it up, the bell stops ringing,' Hawkeye said. 'The bell interferes with my drinking.'

'Horsey and Hot Lips are about twenty minutes out,' Wrong Way reported. 'I just got a call on the radio.'

'That's all I need right now,' Hawkeye said. 'Call them back, Wrong Way, and see if Uncle Hiram is with them.'

'Who's Uncle Hiram?' Wrong Way asked.

'Anybody's Uncle Hiram,' Hawkeye said.

Scarlett's ears, in addition to being (in Bubba's opinion) the cutest ears in the whole wide world, also had the range and sensitivity of those of a fox. She came walking over, with Bubba breathing heavily in her wake.

'Did I hear you say Uncle Hiram, Dr Hawkeye?'

'Perish the thought,' Hawkeye said.

'I would have sworn I heard you say Uncle Hiram,' Scarlett said.

'Hawkeye,' Wrong Way came back on the telephone. 'Affirmative. Your Uncle Hiram is aboard. How come I don't know him?'

Mr Napolitano's voice, coming as it did from a long line of Neapolitan bargemen, was audible anywhere within six feet of the telephone, even though Hawkeye had pressed the earpiece tightly to his head.

'I distinctly heard Uncle Hiram,' Scarlett said.

'My god, I've lost her!' a rather deep, Harvardian voice said, somewhat thickly.

It was Matthew Q. Framingham, making his entrance to Bide-a-While supported by the chauffeur, who was visibly under a strain that threatened to get the best of him at any moment.

'Well, as I live and breathe, if it isn't Matthew Q. Framingham VI,' Trapper John said. 'Whom have you lost?'

'The last thing I remember, there we were in the back seat of the Rolls, singing, "Cigarettes and Whiskey and Wild Wild Women," ' Matthew said. 'And the next thing, I'm here.' He spotted Scarlett and, leaning forward to get a better look, announced, 'My god, they're real!'

Bubba, for some reason, took umbrage at Mr Framingham's remark, even though it could be reasonably argued that it was simply a statement of fact. He expressed his displeasure by punching Mr Framingham in the nose. Mr Framingham fell backward, blood oozing from same.

'Oh, Bubba, you're so strong!' Scarlett said, wonder in her voice.

'What now, oh, wise one?' Trapper John enquired of Hawkeye.

'While the run-of-the-mill bloody nose can be treated with an ice pack,' Hawkeye said, 'there are bloody noses that require hospitalization.'

'And this is one of those cases?'

'I think so,' Hawkeye said. 'Stanley, you and the colonel load Mr Framingham in the ambulance.'

'What about my Polish wedding feast?' Stanley said.

'Take it with you, if you like, in the ambulance,' Hawkeye said. 'We may need it.'

'To the Spruce Harbor Medical Centre?'

'No. We're going to the Greater Montreal General Hospital,' Hawkeye said. 'They've got a fine reputation, bloody nose-wise.'

'Isn't that, what shall I say, making a mountain out of a bloody nose?' Trapper John asked.

'Can you think of any other way we can get from here to Montreal behind flashing red lights on and whooping whooper?' Hawkeye asked.

'For a lousy bloody nose?'

'To save Esther from this bureaucrat who has short-circuited her usual good sense,' Hawkeye said. 'And to get us out of town before you-know-who wakes up, and before you-know-who and her friends arrive.'

'Hurry up, Stanley,' Trapper John snapped. 'You carry Framingham. I'll help with the Polish ham, the roast goose and the vodka.'

Ten minutes later, Spruce Harbor Medical Centre's Ambulance Number Three, with the Framingham Foundation's Rolls-Royce on its bumper, raced out of town at a speed considerably in excess of the fifty-five mph maximum laid down upon the American people by what has been laughingly called the World's Most Exclusive Club.

It had just passed the sign reading, YOU ARE NOW LEAVING SPRUCE HARBOR, GOOD RIDDANCE! when a 747 jumbo jet touched down at Spruce Harbor International and taxied to a parking space.

There came a whirring sound, and a door opened in the bottom of the fuselage. There was another whirring noise, and then a platform on cables was lowered from inside the aircraft. On the platform was a Chevaux Petroleum Company swamp buggy. Even before the platform touched the ground, the driver of the vehicle had started the engine and tried out the air horns.

Mr Napolitano came out to greet the arriving aircraft.

'Hi, Abdullah!' he called out to the driver of the vehicle.

'Up yours, Wrong Way!' His Royal Highness replied warmly, waving at him. And then with a mighty clash of gears and a farewell blast on the air horns, the swamp buggy lurched off.

'Go directly to the hospital,' the Reverend Mother Emeritus Margaret H. W. Wilson ordered, in fluent Abzugian. 'After Horsey buzzed the hospital, Esther will know we're coming anyway.'

No sooner had the peculiar roar of the swamp buggy diesel faded than Wrong Way's ears detected the sound of more aircraft engines. He climbed back up the wooden ladder to the control tower and turned the radio back on.

'Spruce Harbor, this is Borscht Belt Fly Now & Pay

151

Later Airways Number Sixteen for landing and taxi instructions.'

'Go ahead, Borscht Belt.'

'Which runway should I use?'

'How many do you see?'

'All I see is one dirt strip,' the Borscht Belt pilot replied.

'What you see is what you get,' Wrong Way said. 'Welcome to Spruce Harbor!'

'Spruce Harbor, this is Air Force 909 for landing and taxi instructions.'

'Air Force 909, you're number two to land after the Borscht Belt Convair on final.'

'Spruce Harbor, this is Babcock Six. Landing and taxi instructions, please.'

'Babcock Six, hold in the pattern.'

'Far be it from me to suggest in any way that I'm asking for special treatment, Spruce Harbor, but as a matter of incidental intelligence, this is the private, personal aircraft of Mrs Burton Babcock III, chairperson and presidentress of Burton Babcock & Company.'

'In that case, Babcock Six, you might as well divert to, say, Montreal, because you're sure as hell not going to get Wrong Way Napolitano's permission to land here.'

'But Montreal is more than 150 miles, as the crow flies, from here.'

'Be glad I didn't divert you to Seattle, Washington,' Wrong Way replied.

'Do I detect a certain attitude of unfriendliness on your behalf, Spruce Harbor?'

'Let me put it to you this way,' Wrong Way said. 'How would *you* like it if your bride of nearly twenty years, the mother of your children, your companion on life's rocky road, suddenly started to sniff snuff?'

'Babcock Six diverting to Montreal at this time,' Babcock Six said. Instead of landing, then, Babcock Six flew right over Spruce Harbor's runway. He saw the Borscht Belt Convair, the air force Sabreliner, and a familiar airplane.

'Spruce Harbor, how come you let Babcock Learjet Eleven land and I can't?' Babcock Six complained.

'The pilot of Babcock Eleven is an old friend of Stanley K. Warczinski,' Wrong Way replied. 'I made an exception in his case.'

'Oh, I see,' Babcock Six replied. 'Of course, that explains everything.'

'Babcock Six,' another voice came over the radio, 'did I understand you to say that your aircraft is the personal private aircraft of Mrs Josephine Babcock, chairperson and presidentress of Burton Babcock & Company?'

'Affirmative.'

'What's that mean? This is Don Rhotten speaking, and everyone should know by now that I simply can't *stand* people who use big words like that.'

'Affirmative means yes,' the pilot of Babcock Six said.

'Well, why didn't you say so in the first place? If there's one thing Don Rhotten can't stand, it's a smart ass,' Mr Rhotten said. 'Boston area control, this is the Don Rhotten Special. We're going to Montreal, instead of Spruce Harbor. This is Don Rhotten saying good afternoon, and that's the way it is, here at thirty thousand feet, over the rockbound coast of New Hampshire.'

'This is Maine,' Wrong Way chauvinistically corrected him.

'Don Rhotten is never wrong,' Mr Rhotten said. 'If I say it's New Hampshire, it's New Hampshire.'

Although the personal private aircraft of Mrs Burton (Josephine) Babcock III, chairperson and presidentress of Burton Babcock & Company, was going to Montreal, the lady herself was not, at least just then, for she was at that moment, incognito and attired in a white, tie-up-the-back garment, snoring loudly in a room of the Spruce Harbor Medical Centre.

She was not, however, as Hazel had informed Dr McIntyre, passed out. While she had been resting her

153

eyes rather heavily (all through the process of being off loaded from the Framingham Foundation's Rolls, on loaded on to a Spruce Harbor Medical Centre cart, and finally off loaded into bed, where she had been stripped and installed in a hospital gown), she was not what one could truthfully call dead to the world.

At the sounds of a powerful diesel engine, a clashing of gears, and the peal of air horns outside her window, she had, in fact, suddenly returned to full wakefulness. She sat up in bed as if she had been shocked.

Directly across from the foot of the bed was a chest of drawers and a mirror. In it, she saw herself dressed in the hospital gown.

'My god!' she said. 'Where am I?'

God chose not to reply to the interrogatory, and Josephine Babcock was forced to find her own answer to the question. She slid out of the bed and walked on her toes to the door, pulled it open, and peered out. The reception desk of the Medical Centre was perhaps thirty feet away. She shook her head and rubbed her eyes and looked again. She realized that something was seriously wrong with her; she was hallucinating.

Gathered around the receptionist's desk were an odd assortment of people. One was a tall statuesque blonde lady in clerical vestments, including a bishop's *cappa magna*, which was flashing the message 'God Is Love' at five-second intervals. Beside the lady in the flashing bishop's hat was an Arab in full robes. Beside the Arab stood an English gentleman, complete to derby hat and rolled umbrella. Beside the English gentleman was an American Indian gentleman in blue jeans, deerskin shirt and feather in headband. Beside him stood a very large gentleman in an international-distress orange nylon jacket on the back of which was embroidered the legend 'Cajun Air Force'.

As Josephine watched, the gentleman in the Cajun Air Force orange nylon jacket handed the lady a gallon bottle of Old White Stagg Blended Kentucky Bourbon. Holding

154

her *cappa magna*, lights still flashing, in one hand, the lady in the clerical vestments hooked the thumb of her other hand into the ring on the bottle neck, and then hoisted it to her lips. After taking a good four swallows, she passed the bottle to the English gentleman and then contentedly patted her stomach.

As she was doing this, she spotted Josephine Babcock.

'Be right there!' she waved and called out, and came down the corridor to her. 'What can I do for you?' she asked.

'Who are you?' Josephine asked.

'I'm the Reverend Mother Emeritus, actually,' the lady said. 'But since you can't get anybody to answer your ring, I'll come to your assistance. What's wrong with you, anyhow?'

'Nothing's wrong with me,' Josephine exploded.

'Of course not,' the lady said, soothingly. 'Now you just crawl back in bed, dear, like a good girl.'

'I will like hell!' Josephine replied.

'You will either be a good girl and get back in bed,' the lady said, 'or the Reverend Mother will put you back in bed.'

'Now see here,' Josephine said, 'I'm Josephine ... Mrs Burton ... Babcock III, and if you lay a hand on me, I'll break your arm!'

'You're Bubba's mother?' the lady asked. Josephine, shocked, nodded agreement.

The Arab and the English gentleman and the Indian, together with the chap in the orange jacket, came down the corridor.

'Isn't this the most interesting coincidence?' the lady in the vestments said. 'This is Bubba's mother!'

'Up yours!' the Arab gentleman said, handing Josephine a small diamond with a broad smile.

'What did he say?' Josephine asked.

'Don't pay him any attention, dear,' the Reverend Mother Emeritus said. 'He means well.'

'Fat squaw look like Bubba,' Sitting Buffalo said.

'Same white hair. Same teeth. Same big feet.'

A woman wearing a telephone operator's headset on her head came running down the corridor.

'Well?' the Reverend Mother Emeritus asked.

'Hot Lips,' the woman said, 'I just talked to the Bide-a-While.'

'And?'

'Everybody just left in an ambulance. For Montreal.'

'For Montreal? Montreal, Canada? That Montreal?'

'That Montreal,' the lady repeated. 'Something happened to Framingham's nose, and Hawkeye's rushing him to the Greater Montreal General Hospital.'

'Framingham?' Josephine asked. 'Would that possibly be Matthew Q. Framingham VI of the Framingham Theosophical Foundation?'

'As if you didn't know,' the lady with the headset sniffed. 'You should be ashamed of yourself, at your age, carousing around with someone his age!'

'What about Bubba?' Hot Lips asked.

'They went, too. Bubba and his girl-friend and Trapper John. Even Stanley.'

'It must be really serious,' Horsey offered. 'Otherwise, Hawkeye would have brought him here.'

'You're right, Horsey,' Hot Lips said. 'Montreal, here we come!'

'I'm coming, too,' Josephine said. She reached over and snatched the gallon bottle of Old White Stagg Blended Kentucky Bourbon from the English gentleman, who was cradling it in his arms like a baby. She took a swallow neat.

'I think it would be best, dear, if you just crawled back in bed.'

'The next time you call me dear, honey, I'm going to break this jug over your head,' Josephine said. 'Don't you know better than to get between a mother and her Precious Babykins in a situation like this?'

'You may have a point,' Hot Lips said.

'Hot Lips, I wasn't supposed to tell you this,' Hazel

156

said. 'But under the circumstances, I think I'd better. Esther's in Montreal.'

'What's she doing in Montreal?'

'She's going to marry some French-Canadian, who's connected with the provincial government in a communications capacity.'

'Over his dead body, she is!' the English gentleman said. 'Not *my* little prairie flower!' He took a Colt .45 from his belt, made sure it was loaded, and put it back.

'We must all put our personal problems aside in this hour of Matthew Q. Framingham's need,' the Reverend Mother Emeritus said. 'Hazel, you get Esther on the horn, and tell her what's happening. Tell her to set things up at Montreal General and to hold the fort until we get there!'

'Got it,' Hazel replied.

'Let's get this show on the road!' Hot Lips cried, and they all rushed out of the hospital and back into the swamp buggy. On the way back to Spruce Harbor International, they passed two taxi-cabs.

Josephine Babcock recognized Sydney Prescott in the first taxi by her purple hair.

'Why, there's that horrible female,' she said. 'I wonder what she's doing here?'

Uncle Hiram had recognized Ida-Sue Jones in the second taxi.

'I'm happy to hear you say that, ma'am,' he said. 'I'm a Texan and we don't like to badmouth our women. But that one's an exception.'

Chapter Fourteen

Henri Flambeau was not at all pleased with the latest developments in his romance, and for a number of reasons.

The fond romantic dream he had had was to take Esther as his bride in a small ceremony, and then immediately start out on the wedding trip. They would whip right through Spruce Harbor, pausing only long enough for him to add his signature to hers on her cheque account at Spruce Harbor First National Bank and then go directly to Niagara Falls.

He had been more than a little surprised when the doctor she had called to give her away had readily agreed to come. Under the circumstances, there had been nothing for him to do but announce that he was absolutely delighted with the doctor's demonstrated gesture of friendship, even if that meant delaying the ceremony until after two PM, which meant he'd get stuck with another day's rent of the Jean Claude Killy Suite.

It also meant that he would probably have to buy the doctor a post-ceremony drink, and possibly even something to eat. Henri had already promised himself that he was not going to waste a dime of the dowry Esther Flanagan was bringing into their union, so that when, after the *pro forma* night at Niagara Falls, they went on to Florida and the race track at Hialeah, he wouldn't have to associate with the riffraff at the two- and five-dollar windows.

He had, in other words, talked himself into accepting the delay Esther's idiotic notion of being given away would require. He would give in to her little whims with a brave little smile. After the knot was tied, the situation would, of course, be different. *She* would be the one pouring *his* drinks, and lighting *his* cigarettes and, as his wife, of course, it would be out of place for her to keep reminding him that cigarettes are bad for the health.

The telephone rang. Henri Flambeau's heart jumped. He wondered who in the world it could be. There was no way, he reasoned, that any of his ex-wives could know how to find him here, and start bothering him again over alimony and child-support payments. On the other hand, it was entirely possible, he realized, with a sinking feeling in the pit of his stomach, that some busy-body of a desk clerk with nothing better to do with his time could have come across his name on the blacklist of the Greater Montreal Hoteliers & Motel Keepers Association. This was not the moment to get thrown out of the motel.

'I will take that, *Mon Petite Chouchou*,' Henri said, jumping up and dashing to the telephone. 'Hello,' he said, and then, 'What do you mean, who am I and what am I doing in Esther's room?' He then handed the telephone to Esther, with a little bow, and a *very* Gaulic kiss of her hand. 'For you, *Mon Petite Chouchou*,' he said. 'It is the hospital operator again. Perhaps your friend the doctor will not be able to tear himself away after all.'

Esther, her face falling, took the telephone.

'Is something wrong, Hazel?' she asked. A little smile crossed beneath M. Flambeau's neatly-trimmed, carefully old-Grecianed pencil-line moustache.

'Is something wrong, *mon cherie*?' he enquired.

'I'll get right on it, Hazel,' Esther said. 'By the time they get here, I'll have everything arranged for. Thanks for the call.'

'Is something wrong, Esther?' Henri Flambeau asked again, barely disguised hope in every syllable.

'I've got to get right over to the hospital,' Esther said.

159

'Something's happened to Framingham's nose.'

'What hospital? Who is Framingham?'

'Montreal General,' Esther said, walking into the bedroom for her purse.

'And Framingham?'

'He's sort of a friend of mine,' Esther said. 'I'll get back here as soon as I can.'

'But, *Mon Petite Chouchou*,' M. Flambeau said. 'This is our wedding day!'

'There will be time for that later,' Esther said. 'Duty calls!'

'Surely they have nurses as well qualified as you at Montreal General.'

'Far be it from me to suggest that your local nurses are incompetent, Henri,' Esther said. 'But that's not the same thing as saying they're as competent as I am.'

'But to leave me on our wedding day!' Henri said.

'Adieu,' Esther said, rather pleased with the way she was already picking up French. 'I shall return!'

And with that, she was gone.

Although Esther, who was rather unfamiliar with Montreal, was unaware of this, one could practically expectorate from the balcony of the Jean Claude Killy Suite of the Vieux Montreal Howard Johnson's Motel on to the Greater Montreal General Hospital. When she stepped into a taxi in front of the Vieux Montreal and gave instructions to the driver ('Montreal General, and step on it!'), the driver turned and enquired, 'Madame is ill?'

'No, Madame is not ill. Do I look ill?' Esther snapped.

'Madame looks like an American tourist,' the driver replied. 'Is that so?'

'That is so,' Esther said.

'Montreal General Hospital, it is,' the driver said, and sped off. An hour later. after having exposed the American tourist to most of the sights in the old town (including the Maisonneuve Monument, the Seminary of St Sulpice, Jacques Cartier Square and the Lord Nelson Monument) and many of those in the new (including the Museum of Fine Arts, McGill University, the Stone Towers, the Victoria Bridge and the Mount Royal Tunnel), the cab pulled up in front of Greater Montreal General Hospital. The driver was pleased, for he had obviously made a great personal contribution to Canadian-American mutual understanding and it had cost his passenger only $16.50, plus tip.

The pilot of Babcock Number Six had meanwhile flown to Montreal and landed. It had been his intention simply to fuel up the airplane and then get on the telephone and call Burton Babcock & Company to find out what he was supposed to do. His instructions had been to fly to Spruce Harbor, there to await Mrs Babcock. He had, frankly, been rather relieved when he had been denied landing permission. He took pride in the appearance of his airplane and if he had gone into Spruce Harbor, even if he had made it down all right, there was no question in his mind that the airplane would be mud-spattered.

The flight from Spruce Harbor to Montreal had not been uneventful, however. An idiot in another airplane had followed him to Montreal, so closely that he could see the co-pilot, a remarkably ugly bald-headed man with thick glasses and bad teeth, staring at him from the cockpit window.

He decided, after landing, that while he would indeed make every effort to establish contact with Mrs Babcock, he would do so only after he had taken something, say three or four martinis, to calm his nerves. There was a limit to the sacrifices he was willing to make for Burton Babcock & Company, and he had reached it. Just as soon as he had given orders to have the plane refuelled, he stepped outside the transient aircraft building and hopped into a taxi-cab.

Ten seconds later, the ugly, bald-headed man in the thick glasses ran out on to the sidewalk after him, followed by a wheezing fat man.

'Now what?' the fat man asked, breathlessly. 'We've lost him.'

'You forget that you're with Don Rhotten,' the ugly chap said. 'America's Most Beloved Young TV Newsperson, and paid-up member of the Television Newspersons' Association. Finding him and, through him, your buffalo poisoner, will be no problem at all.'

'How's that?'

'Well, the first thing to do is get a hotel room,' Don Rhotten said. 'Do you suppose this strange town has a Howard Johnson's?'

'How is getting a room in a Howard Johnson's going to help us find that pilot and Mrs 'Buffalo-Poisoning' Babcock?'

'Most Howard Johnson Motels, Dummy,' Don Rhotten said, 'have telephones. All I have to do is pick up the telephone, and they're as good as found.'

'How?'

'Why, I just tell our bureau chief here to find them, that's how,' Don Rhotten said. 'You didn't really expect me to go out and look for them myself, did you? My god, that would be betraying the Anchorperson's oath. We never do anything as crude as running down our own stories. There are little people who do that for us.'

'I hope you know what you're doing, Don,' Taylor P. Jambon said.

'I'm Don Rhotten. I always know what I'm doing,' He flagged a taxi-cab. 'Take us to the nearest Howard Johnson's,' Don Rhotten ordered. 'And if you drive slowly and safely I'll give you my autograph. Instead of a tip, of course.'

'The nearest Howard Johnson's is the Vieux Montreal,' the driver replied. 'But I'll have to charge you extra, if that guy's going along.'

'Whatever for?'

'I don't know what that stuff he's eating out of the can is, but I'd hate to tell you what it smells like.'

162

'You refer, sir,' Taylor P. Jambon said, 'to Taylor P. Jambon's most recently discovered gustatory goodie. This happens to be Old Wild Beanos.'

'If you get in my cab with that stuff, Fatso, you're going to have to buy me an aerosol can of Smell-Be-Gone.'

'Damn the expense!' Don Rhotten said. 'Don Rhotten is on assignment. I'll buy you a *case* of Smell-Be-Gone. What are expense accounts for, anyway?'

Chevaux Petroleum's 747 jumbo jet, with Horsey, Hot Lips, Abdullah, Sitting Buffalo, Uncle Hiram and Josephine Babcock aboard was ten minutes behind Mr Rhotten's aircraft.

For Horsey de la Chevaux, going to Canada posed something of a problem. It was one of the very few countries in the world (Russia being another) in which Chevaux Petroleum, International did not operate. Although the Canadian government made overtures on the average of once every two weeks, suggesting that Canada would welcome the formation of a Canadian subsidiary of Chevaux Petroleum, and seemed perfectly willing to make any number of concessions tax-wise, Chevaux Petroleum had always flatly turned them down.

Horsey had never forgiven the Canadians for what they had done to his relatives. The Louisiana Cajuns are descendants of the French who were expelled from Canada by the British; Cajun itself is a bastardization of the term Canadian. When the secretary of state himself had gone to Horsey and told him, bluntly, that it would greatly assist Canadian-American relations if he would begin operations north of the border, Horsey's reply had been succinct and to the point: 'Screw 'em. Let them find their own oil!'

While Horsey was sure that the Canadian government would now be perfectly willing to offer to him whatever courtesies and privileges they could (and he suspected that he was going to need all the courtesies and privileges he could get if he was to get Esther away from the French-

Canadian bureaucrat and into the arms of Uncle Hiram), he was equally sure that there would be strings attached. If they did him favours, he would have to do them a favour, and that meant starting up a Canadian subsidiary. He had privately vowed not to do that.

He came to the decision, also privately, that he would do nothing until he had to. If necessary, he would back down, but not until he had to.

He underestimated two of his friends, both in their understanding of his feelings in the matter, and in their own influence within Canada. No sooner had the 747 become airborne from Spruce Harbor than the Reverend Mother Emeritus and His Royal Highness, Sheikh Abdullah ben Abzug, excused themselves from the poker game with the announcement that it was necessary that the daisies be sprinkled. Horsey was not suspicious; as much as the two of them had socked away, he had expected this sort of bona fide excuse to leave the game.

His Royal Highness, however, did not go to the gentlemen's rest facility. He made his way instead to the flight deck, where he sought out the flight engineer.

'Hey, "Your Nibs," how are you?' the flight engineer said.

'Your mother wears army shoes,' His Royal Highness said, benignly. He pinched the flight engineer's cheek fondly and handed him a small printed card.

'Esteemed sir (or madame),' the card read. 'I regretfully do not speak your language. Would you be so kind as to call (collect) the number I am pointing out to you? May Allah make his face to shine upon you! Sincerely, Abdullah ben Abzug.'

The flight engineer looked where Abdullah was pointing: 'Canada: The Royal Hussidic Embassy, Montreal, 398-3400.'

'You want the embassy, Abdullah?' the flight engineer said. 'You got it.' He picked up the microphone. 'Montreal area control. Let me have a landline please. Get me Montreal, 398-3400.'

164

He handed His Royal Highness the headset once the number began to ring.

'The Royal Hussidic Embassy,' the voice said, in precise Oxfordian diction.

The flight engineer could not, of course, understand what His Nibs was saying, for the Abzugian language, as has been previously reported, consists in the main of grunts, snorts and wheezes, with a belchlike sound for emphasis. All that the flight engineer knew was that His Nibs grunted, snorted, wheezed and belched for thirty seconds or so, and then handed him the headset back, looking pleased and relieved.

'Up yours!' His Nibs said. He handed the flight engineer an uncut ruby, no more than thirty or forty carats, and added, 'wear it in good health!'

'I can't take this, Your Nibs,' the flight engineer replied, handing it back. His Royal Highness looked disappointed. He took it back, smiled, pinched him on the cheek again, and handed him an emerald of about the same size. Then, before this could be returned, he quickly left the flight deck.

As he went through the door, the Reverend Mother Emeritus came the other way.

'Can you get me a telephone number in Montreal, Larry!' she asked. 'I don't want Horsey to know about it.'

'You got it, Hot Lips,' the flight engineer said.

'Montreal Missionary Temple,' a light and somewhat lisping voice announced. 'GILIAFCC, Inc., God loves you. Brother Bobbie speaking. I love you, too.'

'Bobbie, guess who this is!'

'Reverend Mother Emeritus, is that really you?'

'In the flesh.'

'What can I do for you?'

'Get out your pencil, Bobbie,' the Reverend Mother said. 'I've got a long list.'

Ten minutes behind the Chevaux 747 were, of course, the Borscht Belt Fly Now & Pay Later Airways aircraft and the Air Force Congressional VIP Flight aircraft carrying, respectively, Sydney Prescott, Lance Fairbanks, Brucie (who was, to Sydney's undisguised disgust, airsick again) and Congressman and Mrs Alamo Jones. Mrs Jones, quite naturally, had ordered the pilot to inform the United States consul in Montreal that they were about to be honoured with the in-the-flesh presence of Congressman Jones, and that all necessary arrangements (such as arranging for, and paying for, hotel accommodations and rental cars) should be made as a matter of the highest priority.

One of the first things a junior foreign-service officer learns is that whenever a Congressman leaves either his home district or our nation's capitol he makes this sacrifice only as an official duty, and thus expects not only the taxpayer to pick up the tab, but the foreign service to serve as sort of a private congressional travel agency.

So when the very junior foreign-service officer learned that Montreal was about to be honoured with the presence of Congressman Jones, he looked him up and found that on a scale of 435, the congressman ranked, influence-wise, somewhere around thirteenth from the bottom. The Vieux Montreal Motel, offering as it did such a splendid view of Greater Montreal General Hospital from its off-street windows, was under that happenstance just the thing for the congressman and his party. The Vieux Montreal did not offer room service. Congressmen, as a class, the young officer had learned, went absolutely bananas with room service while travelling in the public service. It was important, therefore, the junior foreign-service officer had learned at the foreign-service school,* that access to room service be limited to only those congressmen who could influence one's promotion, or the promotion of one's immediate superior.

'One of your economy rooms, Charles,' the junior

---

* Specifically, in course 201.011. Intermediate Practical Diplomacy III: Intergovernmental Relationships, Especially with Congress.

foreign-service officer said to the manager of the Vieux Montreal Motel. 'And if this one does any boozing, you'd better advise him beforehand that our counterpart* funds are exhausted and he'll have to pay for it himself.'

As the two were chatting on the telephone, Henri Flambeau was leaning on the railing of the balcony of the Jean Claude Killy Suite, a pencil-thin cigar in one hand, a snifter of brandy in the other, thinking happily of the bangtails at Hialeah he would shortly see.

The sound of approaching sirens reached his ears, causing him to hastily toss down the brandy in his glass, and to move away from the railing to a position where, if by any chance the officers of the law had been dispatched by any one of his wives or the judge of Domestic Relations Court making good his no-child-support slammer-time threat was seeking him, he could take a flying leap off the balcony and make his escape.

But the sirens were not for him. Peering through the wrought-Old World-cast aluminium railing, he saw a rather astonishing sight. Four Royal Canadian Mounted Police in their famous red coats aboard Kawasaki motorcycles, preceded the longest, blackest Rolls-Royce Henri had ever seen. A thickly embroidered flag flew from the

---

* Counterpart funds, being as it is one of the more imaginative ploys of our government, deserves explanation. From time to time, foreign nations, either struck by conscience or, more ordinarily, stuck with an excess of non-negotiable currency (San Sebastian *bananarios*, for example, or imperial Russian promissory notes), use these funds as token payments on their indebtedness to the United States of America. The funds are not, however, deposited in the US treasury, but rather retained by the US embassy in the 'repaying' country. They are then used to pay the bills of congressmen and other governmental officials who find themselves serving their country on alien shores. Since the money actually repaid is frequently less valuable than the shoe boxes in which it is packed, and unacceptable to hotel keepers, bartenders and so on, the American ambassador makes a like, or counterpart amount of real (*ie*, American) money available to our travelling solons. This arrangement permits our congressmen to truthfully announce that not one taxpayer's dollar went to pay for, for example, his evening at the opera, the cashmere sweaters he sent all his relatives, or the little souvenir gift he gave his interpreter for all her courtesies and kindnesses to him.

167

Rolls' front fender. He had never seen anything like it. There was a gold-embroidered pair of crossed scimitars.* Above the scimitars was a gold-embroidered representation of what looked like an oil-well drilling rig and, above that, a gold-embroidered dollar sign.

Two Cadillac limousines followed the Rolls-Royce, and four more Royal Canadian Mounted Police brought up the rear. The Rolls-Royce pulled up to the door of the Vieux Montreal, and the two Cadillac limousines pulled up behind it. From the rearmost limousine a tall, rather bony-featured chap in a frock coat, striped trousers and beret emerged and ran to the Rolls-Royce.

'*Mon dieu!*' Henri Flambeau said. 'That looks like Monsieur le Prime Minister himself!' This snap judgement was confirmed when the man snatched off his beret as he pulled the door of the Rolls open. Henri could see the Cheshire-cat grin. Henri strained to hear what was being said.

'Your Royal Highness,' the premier said, 'your slightest wish is our command. If you wish to make the Vieux Montreal Howard Johnson Motel your temporary royal palace, so be it!'

'Your mother wears army boots,' a deep voice boomed, and Henri saw a very large Arab, in full Arabian costume, get out of the Rolls.

'How good of you to say so, Your Highness,' the premier said, flashing his famous smile again.

An English gentleman, complete to derby and rolled umbrella, next got out of the limousine. Henri had heard that most Arab oil kings had British advisers, and that explained who this chap must be. He was also, Henri saw, obviously doubling as the Arab's bodyguard, for the butt of a large revolver was visible, sticking out of his belt just below the pearl grey vest.

The doors of the first Cadillac limousine opened and four people got out. A large lady in a hospital gown, a

* Scimitars are those curved swords one sees in motion-picture epics dealing with the Sahara Desert and the Arabs.

striking blonde in nurse's whites (obviously the lady's personal nurse), a large man wearing an orange flight jacket (obviously the Arab's personal pilot), and an Indian, complete with feather headband (Henri had no idea whom he might be).

'Horsey,' the nurse ordered, 'you get everybody settled, and keep them in the hotel. I'll go look after Framingham.'

'You got it, Hot Lips,' the chap in the orange jacket said. He walked up to the Arab, opened his mouth, and a series of strange grunts, snorts and wheezes, punctuated by burps, came out.

The Arab nodded his head. 'You got it, Hot Lips!' he said, gesturing regally at her. 'Up yours!'

'I beg your pardon, sir,' the premier said to the man in the orange jacket. 'But you bear the most remarkable resemblance to Colonel Jean-Pierre de la Chevaux.'

'No speaka da English,' the man in the orange jacket said, and taking the Arab's arm, propelled him into the motel. The Englishman and the lady in the hospital gown followed him. The nurse got into the Rolls-Royce. The premier bowed again and closed the door. The window whooshed down. The nurse's head appeared. 'OK, you clowns!' she shouted. 'Let's get this show on the road! Montreal General, and don't spare the horses!'

Chapter Fifteen

'Every time I think that I may be losing my position as America's Most Beloved Young TV Newsperson,' Don Rhotten said to Taylor P. Jambon, 'something like this happens to reassure me!'

'What are you talking about, Don?' Taylor P. Jambon said.

'Look at all those Royal Canadian Mounted Police in those *darling* red coats and Smokey the Bear hats gathered around the Vieux Montreal Howard Johnson's to protect me from my fans!' Don Rhotten said. 'Quick, hand me my wig, I wouldn't dream of disappointing them!'

'Here's the rug,' Taylor said, 'but what are you going to do about your teeth and eyeglasses?'

'I'll keep my mouth shut,' Don Rhotten said. 'And you sort of steer me through the hordes of my adoring fans.'

Taylor P. Jambon decided that it was a good thing there hadn't been time for Don Rhotten to insert his Paul Newman-blue contact lenses. Without them he had been unable to see the looks of undisguised contempt on the Mounties' faces as he was led past them, announcing that there was just no time to give his autograph. Don was always crushed at the slightest hint that he wasn't as beloved as he liked to think he was. And Don Rhotten, ego crushed, was just hell to be around; Taylor P. Jambon could not stand to watch a grown man cry.

Almost as soon as they had been shown to their suite and Don had rushed to the bathroom so that he could put in his contacts and caps, 'so that I can, at least,' as he put it, 'give those police persons the thrill of having me wave at them from the balcony,' there was a knock at the door.

Taylor P. Jambon answered it.

'Oh,' said a rather good-looking chap with a pencil-line moustache, who spoke with a French accent. 'It *is* you, Mr Jambon!'

'Who are you? Do you always talk that funny? And what do you want?'

'I am one of your most devoted fans,' he replied. 'My name is Henri Flambeau, and I have taken it upon myself, as one of your most devoted fans, to welcome you to Montreal and to put myself at your disposal.'

'Who's that out there with you?' Don Rhotten called from the john.

'A fan, Don,' Taylor P. Jambon said.

'Tell him no autographs at this time, and try to sell him a copy of my book,'* Don Rhotten called.

'One of *my* fans,' Taylor called, not without just a smidgen of pride in his voice.

'Taylor, I'm here on a big story,' Don Rhotten called. 'I have no time to dally with one of your food-freak fatties.'

'You say you're really one of my big fans?' Taylor asked.

'Oh, yes, sir,' Henri Flambeau said. 'I've watched every one of your shows at least three times.'

'You don't say?'

'I do say,' Henri repeated. 'And I was afraid to believe it was really you when I saw you leading that poor blind man into the motel.'

'Luck was with you,' Taylor said. 'It is I.'

---

* Mr Rhotten here referred to his autobiography, *Presidents and Other Biggies Who Have Known Me*. (Published in 1975, the book is no longer in print. Mr Rhotten, however, acquired the remainder stock of some 135,400 copies, and makes them available to the public whenever possible.)

Don Rhotten came out of the bathroom. 'You say you're one of Taylor's fans?' he asked.

'Yes, sir, I am,' Henri said.

'Then this is really a big day for you, isn't it?' Don asked. 'I mean with both of us.'

'I'm always happy to meet another Taylor P. Jambon fan,' Henri said.

'I'm not a fan,' Don snapped. 'I'm Don Rhotten.'

'I thought I did detect a certain odour,' Henri said.

'Oh, that's the Wild West Beanos,' Taylor said. 'I'll give you a little taste.'

As Henri Flambeau dipped appreciatively into the can of Wild West Beanos, finally pursing his lips to kiss the air as a symbol of his appreciation of the product, Don Rhotten stared at him appraisingly.

'No offence, Mr Jambon,' Henri said, 'and I wouldn't ask if this didn't happen to be my wedding day, but your fan here is all right, isn't he? I mean, despite that perfume he's wearing. I would be crushed to learn that a fellow Taylor P. Jambon fan was, how shall I say, a fairy?'

'Don walks a little strange,' Taylor said. 'But put your mind to rest.'

'Then why is he staring at me that way?'

'How would you like to be on television?' Don Rhotten asked.

'What are you talking about, Don?' Taylor asked.

'Your fan with the funny moustache and that weird accent may be just what I'm looking for,' Don said.

'I thought you said he was all right,' Henri said.

'For what, Don?' Taylor asked.

'I always like to get the reaction of the man on the street to one of my stories,' Don Rhotten said. 'But there are problems when I do that. The man on the street usually says the wrong thing.'

'I think I'm beginning to see what you're talking about,' Taylor P. Jambon said.

'Just off the top of your head, Frenchie . . .' Don

Rhotten said, and then stopped at the sound of a strange sound – a deep cowlike mooing. 'What the hell is that?' he asked.

Taylor P. Jambon ran to the door and opened it a crack. Then he slammed it quickly again.

'Well?'

'It was two Royal Canadian Mounted Police with a buffalo* on a leash,' he said.

'I don't believe it!' Don Rhotten said, and went and looked for himself. Then he turned and said, 'Who said God's not on my side?'

'You lost me somewhere along the way, Don,' Taylor said.

'Taylor, you do have some of that stuff, that *soja hispida Babcockisis*, don't you?'

'I've got a fifty-pound sack of it,' Taylor P. Jambon said.

'Great!' Don Rhotten said. 'We now have two of the three ingredients we need to win me my Emmy and my rightful place on the "One Hour" show.'

'What are you talking about, Don?'

'Frenchie,' Don said, 'I realize this may come at you a little fast because I'm a genius, and you're anything but, but do you think you could make believe you're a veterinarian?'

'A vegetarian?'

'*Veterinarian*,' Don Rhotten said. 'A doggie doctor, but for buffaloes, instead.'

'You are trying to mislead people,' Henri Flambeau said. 'That is dishonest.'

'You mean you won't do it?' Don Rhotten said, visibly disappointed. 'You and your honest fans, Taylor!'

'I didn't say that,' Henri said. 'I was about to ask, what's in it for me? And what exactly do I have to do?'

'All you have to say is something like this: "In all of

---

* This was, of course, Teddy Roosevelt, who had been left behind at the airport until a truck could be found to carry him along to the Vieux Montreal Motel.

173

my professional experience, I have never seen a buffalo in greater agony." Do you think you could remember all of that?'

'In all of my many years of professional experience, in all corners of the globe, I can state without qualification that I have never seen a buffalo in greater agony,' Henri Flambeau, who was, after all, a card-carrying member of Montreal Local 313, Advertising Modelpersons of the World, ad-libbed. He had been quick to see this for what it was. He was about to be asked to do a dog-food commercial. And as every aspiring actor knows, the route to TV stardom is paved with dog-food commercials. Perhaps, just perhaps, he would not actually have to go through with his marriage to the fat redheaded nurse.

'Great!' Don Rhotten said.

'And what's in it for me?'

'How does a hundred bucks sound?' Don Rhotten said.

'Not as nice as five hundred,' Henri Flambeau said. 'Plus residuals.'

'Two fifty,' Don Rhotten said.

'Four hundred, and you've got yourself a veterinarian,' Henri said.

'Done,' Don Rhotten said. They shook hands.

'Let me see if I can get this straight in my mind,' Henri said, 'I am, of course, a devotee of the Pavlovian School of Acting.'

'Don't you mean Stanislavsky?' Taylor P. Jambon asked.

'Whatever. What I'm trying to say is that I have to feel the part,' Henri said.

'All you have to do is stand there in a doggie-doctor jacket and say you never saw a buffalo in greater agony,' Don Rhotten said. 'What's so hard about that? This is the news, not "As the World Turns"!'

'Don,' Taylor said. 'You said you had two of the three things you need. What's missing?'

'Mrs Josephine Babcock,' Don said. 'But we know

174

she's here. Her plane is here. She must be here. All I have to do is find her. I'll get right on that. Just as soon as we find her, we feed the buffalo some of that *soja hispida Babcockisis* right in front of her very eyes, Frenchie here delivers that line about the buffalo's agony, and then I ask her, "How about that, Mrs Babcock?" That'll teach her not to cancel her TV cigarette advertising.'

'Fair's fair, Don,' Taylor P. Jambon said. 'She didn't willingly cancel the advertising. The government made her.'

'Nonsense, you know as well as I do that interfering with television's profits is unAmerican,' Don Rhotten said. Before Taylor P. Jambon could pursue the argument further, Don Rhotten had grabbed the telephone and been connected with the ABS News Montreal bureau: 'Don Rhotten here,' he announced. 'I want you to locate a Mrs Josephine Babcock, also known as Mrs Burton Babcock III . . .' There was a pause. 'How should I know where to look for her? That's not my problem. That's what you people are for. I have enough to do reading the scripts and coming up with brilliant ideas like this one. Find her, that's all. And send a camera crew over here right away with a doggie-doctor jacket. Yeah, that's what I said, a doggie-doctor jacket. And then tell ABS to stand by for a live bulletin story.'

Although, of course, there was no way Mr Rhotten could have known this, Mrs Josephine Babcock was, at that very moment, right above him, in the Sky-Vue Suite of the Vieux Montreal Howard Johnson's Motel.

Her white hospital gown had been replaced by one of His Royal Highness' caftans. Horsey had offered, as he put it, to 'spring for some duds' from any Montreal store of her choosing, but Josephine had replied that she hadn't worn off-the-rack clothing since her marriage and she had no intention of starting now. There was spare clothing aboard her plane, and she would wait until she got that.

175

A game of chance, which Horsey had suggested as a means to pass time until things could be sorted out, was in progress. While Mrs Babcock's luck with the cards had been entirely pleasant to experience, she was growing more and more annoyed with the Arab and Horsey, who were carrying on what presumably was a conversation, but which sounded like nothing more than grunts, snorts and wheezes. She presumed that the game was being discussed. She erred.

'I admire this lady, Horsey,' His Royal Highness was saying in Abzugian.

'She's all right, I suppose,' Horsey replied in Abzugian.

'Who would I see about buying her?' His Royal Highness replied. He beamed at Josephine, switched to English, and spoke to the lady. 'Your mother wears army boots,' he said.

'Tell him if he says that to me one more time, Horsey, I'll break this bottle over his head.'

Delighted with the response, His Royal Highness smiled again, pinched Josephine on the cheek and spoke the second of the three English phrases he had memorized.

'Up yours!' he said, whereupon Josephine made good her threat. A half-gallon bottle of Old White Stagg Blended Kentucky Bourbon flew through the air, smashed down upon His Royal Highness' royal headgear, and shattered. The contents of the nearly full bottle ran down His Royal Highness' face and soaked his royal robes even as His Royal Highness slid under the table.

'Never did like playing cards with women,' Uncle Hiram said. 'There's trouble every time.'

Josephine was immediately sorry for what she had done. As Abdullah's somewhat bloodshot eyeballs rolled upward in his head, she had a sudden, sickening fear that she had killed him.

'Oh, my god,' she cried. 'I've killed him.'

Horsey felt Abdullah's pulse.

'He's alive,' he reported. 'I guess all that money he carried around in his hat broke the blow.'

'I'll raise twenty bucks,' Uncle Hiram said.

'Your twenty and twenty more, white man,' Sitting Buffalo said.

'How can you simply go on playing cards under these circumstances?' Josephine replied. She glanced disparagingly at the cards in her hand. And then glanced again. 'Your twenty and twenty on top, Sitting Buffalo. That makes it sixty to you, Horsey.'

'I'll call,' Horsey said.

'Read 'em and weep,' Josephine said. 'King high flush.' She then stood up and went to the door. She pulled it open. The Royal Canadian Mounted Police on duty in the corridor came to attention.

'You there, in the Nelson Eddy suit,' Josephine said. 'There has been a slight accident in here.'

The Royal Canadian Mountie came into the room. He saw Abdullah on the floor. When he bent over him, the fumes of the Old White Stagg assailed his nostrils.

'I thought these people didn't drink,' he said. 'I should have known better.' He took his whistle and blew on it. Two more Royal Canadian Mounties came running up.

'We'd better run this guy over to Montreal General,' the first Mountie said. 'But it'll take four of us to carry him. Where's Antoine?'

'Walking the buffalo,' a second Mountie replied.

'You want to give us a hand, fella?' the first Mountie said to Sitting Buffalo, who was closest.

'Screw you, white man,' Sitting Buffalo replied.

'Horsey,' Josephine said. 'Help these people carry this man!'

'You hit him,' Horsey replied, reasonably. 'You help them!'

'Very well,' Josephine sniffed.

'Oh, hell,' Uncle Hiram said. 'The game's ruined anyhow. You get one leg, Sitting Buffalo, and I'll get the other, and don't hand *me* none of that "Screw you, white man" business either.' He patted the Colt .45 in his belt.

'You go get the ambulance started, Phillipe,' the senior Mountie said. 'And while these weirdos are carrying His Royal Highness downstairs, I'll call Montreal General and tell them we're coming.'

Carrying His Royal Highness between them, two of the Royal Canadian Mounties, Sitting Buffalo and Uncle Hiram left the suite and went down the corridor to the elevator, with Josephine hovering over them. It was immediately apparent that all six of them would never get into the elevator at once.

'Down the stairs!' one of the Mounties cried.

The stairs were in plain view of the balcony of Mr Rhotten's suite, on which he and Henri Flambeau were rehearsing Mr Flambeau's doggie-doctor bit.

'My god, that's her,' Don Rhotten suddenly cried.

'I don't have that cue in my script,' Henri Flambeau said. 'If I've got more lines, that's going to cost you more money.'

'Taylor!' Don Rhotten shouted. 'There's Josephine Babcock, the buffalo poisoner, herself.'

'Where?'

'In her bathrobe, with that guy the Royal Mounties are carrying down the stairs. I guess they always do get their man, after all.'

'Now that you've found her, Don,' Taylor P. Jambon said, 'don't you think you'd better hang on to her?'

'Good thinking, Jambon,' Don Rhotten said. 'I'll follow them. You round up the buffalo and bring Frenchie and the camera crew along.'

'Where will you be?' Taylor P. Jambon said.

'I won't know that until I get there, now, will I?' Don Rhotten replied, and started for the stairs.

Margaret Houlihan Wachauf Wilson, RN it will be recalled, had gone on to the hospital approximately an hour before. She was expected. A very large gentleman, with a British brush moustache, his light green jacket

178

identifying him as a senior member of the medical staff, was standing just inside the plate-glass doors.

'Nurse Wilson,' he said, in a deep voice. 'We have been waiting for you. I'm placing the facilities of the hospital at your disposal.'

This was not the sort of response Nurse Wilson was used to (except perhaps at New Orleans' Gates of Heaven Hospital, where it was generally known that she and the Reverend Mother Bernadette of Lourdes, MD, FACS and chief of staff, were buddies) and she was surprised.

'Why, that's very kind of you, Doctor,' she said.

The doctor leaned forward and whispered in her ear. 'I wouldn't want it broadcast all over,' he said, 'but I'm one of yours, Reverend Mother Emeritus!'

'God bless you,' Nurse Wilson boomed.

'Brother Bobbie called me from the Temple,' the doctor said.

'Has the patient arrived?' Hot Lips asked.

'No, not yet,' the doctor replied. 'And . . . I don't know how to tell you this, but we're having a little problem with the other nurse. The redheaded one.'

'What sort of a problem?'

'The truth of the matter is, she's been drinking,' the doctor said.

'Drinking? Esther Flanagan, RN? Is that who you're talking about?'

'I'm afraid so,' the doctor said.

'I refuse to believe that Esther Flanagan, RN would booze it up on duty!'

'She was already pretty plastered when Brother Bobbie called and told me you were coming,' the doctor said. 'And for the past half hour, she's been on a crying jag.'

'Take me to her!' Hot Lips ordered.

'I managed to get her to go to my private office,' the doctor said. 'Right this way.'

Esther Flanagan, when the doctor opened his office door and ushered Hot Lips in, was seated at the doctor's desk. She had somehow acquired a set of nursing whites. The crisp nurse's cap which was designed to be worn atop the head, was on one side, apparently defying the laws of gravity. Tears ran down Esther's face. Her right hand grasped a glass, her left, a bottle of whiskey.

'Esther!' Hot Lips said.

'Men are no damned good!' Esther said.

'Why, I know that, dear,' Hot Lips said. 'But what has that got to do with you being in, how shall I phrase it, your present disgusting condition?'

'And French-Canadian men are the worst of all!' Esther went on.

'Tell me all about it, dear,' Hot Lips said.

'By god, there's another one!' Esther said, finally focusing her eyes on the doctor standing behind Hot Lips. She picked up the whiskey bottle, and took aim with it.

'He's all right, Esther,' Hot Lips said, quickly. 'He's one of mine.'

'That's what he says! You can't believe a word they say, believe you me!'

'Perhaps it would be best if I left you alone,' the doctor said. 'I'll wait in the corridor.'

Hot Lips picked up the telephone. 'Get some coffee in here,' she ordered. 'Lots of it, and as black as possible. What do you mean, who am I? I'm the Reverend Mother Emeritus, that's who the hell I am!'

'He lied to me, Hot Lips,' Esther said.

'They all do that, dear,' Hot Lips replied. 'I could have told you that.'

'I trusted him.'

'Start at the beginning,' Hot Lips said. 'And tell me all about it.'

'Just as soon as I got the call about Framingham's nose,' Esther said, rather thickly, 'I came right over here.'

'I see. And had you had a little something to settle your stomach before you came?'

'I was as sober as a judge,' Esther said, righteously.

'Go on.'

'So I told them who I was, and what I wanted. I told them I didn't know what was wrong with Framingham's nose, but if Hawkeye and Trapper John were coming all this way, it must be pretty serious.'

'I see. I don't know what's wrong with his nose yet, either,' Hot Lips said.

'So I told them I wanted an operating room all set up, and that we'd probably need a gas-passer. You know, the whole routine.'

'And?'

'They told me that they couldn't do that without additional information,' Esther said. 'So then I remembered what Henri had told me about his being connected with the provincial government in a communications capacity – having influence, I mean.'

'So?'

'So I used his name,' Esther said. 'And they checked the list of important bureaucrats, and he wasn't on that. And then they checked the list of minor bureaucrats, and he wasn't on that, either.'

'That's odd,' Hot Lips said.

'And then some doctor came. You can't tell it by looking at him, but he's one of yours, Hot Lips.'

'That must be the fellow who met me at the door,' Hot Lips said.

'And he said that any friend of yours was a friend of his, and he would personally look into the matter for me.'

'And did he straighten it out?'

'Henri has three wives and six children,' Esther said. 'And, that connection with the provincial government in a communications capacity he told me about? He sells money orders in the post office, that's what he does?'

'Oh, Esther,' Hot Lips said.

'So I had a little drink to settle my nerves,' Esther said. 'And then another. Perhaps three in all.'

The door opened and a nurse's helper brought in a tray holding a pot of coffee and some cups.

'Doctor,' Hot Lips called. 'Are you still out there?'

'At your service, Reverend Mother Emeritus!'

'Far be it from me to suggest a course of treatment to you, Doctor,' Hot Lips said. 'I'm sure you've already considered cold-water therapy in this case yourself.'

'I have,' he said. 'But she sent three nurses fleeing.'

'She'll be a good girl now, won't you, Esther?' Hot Lips said. There was no reply. When Hot Lips turned, Esther had laid her head on the desk. Her eyes were closed. A snore, and then another, came from her.

'I'll get a wagon,' the doctor said. 'And let me say, Reverend Mother Emeritus, that I knew you would succeed where we all had failed.'

'Just tie her to the cart,' Hot Lips said, professionally. 'And roll her under the shower.'

Chapter Sixteen

On the outskirts of Montreal, in the opinion of the attending physicians, Hawkeye Pierce and Trapper John McIntyre, the condition of Matthew Q. Framingham VI's nose had improved to the point where hospitalization was no longer medically indicated.

'Well,' Hawkeye, who was driving the ambulance, said over the CB to Trapper John, who was driving the Rolls-Royce. 'Good buddy, there doesn't seem to be much else we can do but find a motel, does there? Come back.'

'There's a sign reading Vieux Montreal Howard Johnson's Motel, good buddy,' Trapper John said.

'Isn't that an interesting coincidence?' Hawkeye said. 'This is the Ol' Pecker Checker going Ten-ten.'

The little convoy rolled up at the Vieux Montreal just moments after the ambulance carrying His Royal Highness had sped off. The sound of the siren, so to speak, still hung in the air.

'You keep your eye on Bubba and Scarlett, Trapper,' Hawkeye said. 'Get them to help Stanley unload the Polish wedding feast. I would prescribe a cold shower, but they'd probably get in it together. I will run down Esther and see what I can do about cooling her off until she comes to her senses.'

As Hawkeye walked into the motel, he glanced casually into the patio. As he approached the desk to enquire as to Miss Flanagan's room number, he realized that he had really been under a mental strain lately. It was absolutely inconceivable, of course – his brain was playing tricks on him – but there was just no way that he could have seen Taylor P. Jambon, America's Most Famous TV Gourmet and a Royal Canadian Mounted Policeman trying to dissuade a buffalo from eating the Vieux Montreal's shrubbery.

'Miss Flanagan's room, please,' Dr Pierce said, shaking his head.

'She's in the Jean Claude Killy Suite, sir,' the desk clerk said. 'But she's not there. About two hours ago, she rushed to the Montreal General Hospital.'

'Oh?'

'We've been busy-busy here today,' the desk clerk confided. 'Medical emergency-wise. Why, just two minutes ago, we rushed His Royal Highness Sheikh Abdullah ben Abzug, the personal guest of His Excellency, our prime minister, away by ambulance.'

'What happened to him?'

'Far be it from me, sir, to discuss the drinking habits of our guests,' the desk clerk said, 'but if you'll just sniff, sir, the fumes that surrounded His Royal Highness are still very much in the atmosphere.'

Hawkeye sniffed. 'Old White Stagg,' he said. 'Tell me, was there a guy in an orange flight jacket with him?'

'No, sir,' the desk clerk said. 'Not that I can recall. There was an English gentleman hanging on to one leg, as I remember, and an Indian gentleman on the other. Two of our Royal Canadian Mounted Police each had an arm. But no one in an orange flight jacket.'

Hawkeye turned away from the desk. Trapper John was holding the door for Bubba, Scarlett, Matthew Q. Framingham, Col. Merritt T. Charles and Stanley K. Warczinski.

'Stanley,' Hawkeye said. 'Something has come up. You're going to have to keep those two apart by yourself.'

Stanley K. Warczinski looked at Hawkeye with total incomprehension in his eyes. He opened his mouth. A belch resounded around the room. Stanley K. Warczinski

184

had obviously been tasting the vodka to make sure that it wasn't going bad.

'Oh, hell, Stanley,' Hawkeye said. 'Matthew, you and the colonel unload that stuff. Bubba, you and Scarlett come with us.'

'Where are we going?'

'Over to the hospital,' Hawkeye said. 'Esther's there.'

In the swimming pool patio, meanwhile, Teddy Roosevelt had raised his head from Howard Johnson's evergreens to sniff the air. It was as if he had detected a familiar and pleasing smell.

Hawkeye, Trapper John, Bubba and Scarlett rushed back out of the motel. Teddy Roosevelt saw Scarlett. His tail began to wag. He started out after her, dragging Taylor P. Jambon and the Royal Canadian Mounted Policeman after him.

As Hawkeye pulled open the door to the Rolls-Royce, Trapper John asked a passer-by directions to Montreal General.

'You can walk there quicker than driving,' the passer-by replied, indicating the hospital with his hand.

The four started out across the wide lawn for the hospital as Teddy Roosevelt, dragging Taylor P. Jambon and the Mountie after him, emerged from the motel. And as Teddy Roosevelt, picking up a little speed now, started after Scarlett, a truck bearing the familiar ABS logotype on its side pulled into the driveway.

'Do you suppose that's the buffalo we're after, Lucien?' the cameraman asked.

'How many buffaloes can one expect to find in a Howard Johnson's, Alphonse?' Lucien, the sound man, replied. 'After them!'

At the hospital, meanwhile, forty-five minutes under a cold shower and about a gallon and a half of coffee had done wonders for what Hot Lips chose to call 'Esther's delicate condition.' It had not done much good for her feeling of humiliation, however.

'Go ahead, Hot Lips,' she said. 'Push me under the shower again. I deserve to be drowned, or to catch pneumonia.'

'Nonsense, dear,' Hot Lips said. 'We are all sinners, as I said myself just the other day. I'm not pushing you under the shower for punishment, but to make sure that you're . . . on the road to recovery.'

The telephone rang. The doctor answered it.

'We just got a message to expect an unconscious patient reeking of alcohol,' he said.

'That's obviously Hawkeye with Matthew Q. Framingham,' Hot Lips said. She turned to Esther. 'Duty calls, Esther,' she said, sternly. 'Are you up to meeting it, or should I roll you under the cold shower again?'

'I can do my duty,' Esther said. 'After which I will shoot myself. I have disgraced myself beyond redemption.'

'Get dressed and join us,' Hot Lips said. 'And we'll have no more of that kind of talk.'

'I might as well,' Esther said, 'shoot myself, I mean. I not only have gotten drunk when duty called, but lost my last chance for l'amour.'

'Have I got news for you!' Hot Lips said.

'You don't have that dirty old cowboy with you, do you?' Esther said. 'That settles it. Where can I find a gun?'

Meanwhile, back at the Vieux Montreal, Sydney Prescott recognized, with an enormous sense of relief, a familiar face. The last place she expected to find Col. Merritt T. Charles was in the act of carrying a roast goose into a Montreal motel, but there was no question that it was him.

'Hi, there, Baldy,' she said. 'Remember me? Sydney Prescott?'

'Unfortunately,' the colonel replied.

'You haven't seen ol' Bubba lately, have you?'

'Why should I tell you?'

'Because you know I'm working for Mrs Burton

Babcock III in this matter,' she said. That would, under ordinary circumstances, have been enough to seal the colonel's lips forever. But he saw Lance Fairbanks and Brucie behind Sydney Prescott.

'Are those two with you?' he asked.

'Yes, indeed.'

'You can find Bubba over at the hospital,' the colonel said, with a warm smile. The mental image of Lance and Brucie violating the six-foot rule brought a smile to the colonel's face, and he whistled cheerfully as he carried the roast goose into the motel.

Hot Lips was waiting in the emergency room for the unconscious patient reeking of alcohol when he was carried in. It was not, of course, Matthew Q. Framingham, but Abdullah. As she rolled back his eyelid to look into his eyes, the patient woke up.

'What have you been up to Abdullah, you naughty boy?' Hot Lips asked, in Abzugian.

'I have changed my mind, Hot Lips,' His Royal Highness said. 'I don't wish to buy her after all. She has a nasty temper. I already have eight wives with nasty tempers and that's more than enough.'

'What did he say? What did he say?' Josephine Babcock asked.

'He said you have a nasty temper and he doesn't want to buy you, after all,' Hot Lips said.

'Well, I've never been so insulted in my life!' Josephine said.

'Stick around,' Hot Lips said. 'I haven't had a chance to warm up on you.'

The door to the emergency room burst open. Hawkeye and Trapper John came in.

'Hi ya, Hot Lips, what's up?'

'She broke a bottle over Abdullah's head,' Hot Lips said. 'No harm done.'

Bubba and Scarlett came in.

'Mother,' Bubba said. 'Whatever are you doing here, and in an Arabian robe?'

'She hit the Arab with a bottle, Bubba,' Hot Lips said. 'God alone knows why.'

'At your age!' Scarlett said. 'Mother Babcock, you should be ashamed of yourself!'

'Mother, I must tell you, I'm shocked,' Bubba said. 'The least you could have done is conceal your lover's quarrels from public view! Wait until it gets around the ladies' lounge of the Burton Babcock III Memorial Yacht, Tennis & Golf Club that you chased your Arabian boyfriend to Canada and then broke a bottle over his head in a lover's quarrel!'

'I didn't come to Canada with that Arab!'

'Wearing nothing but a hospital nightgown, too,' Scarlett said. 'Mother Babcock!'

'I came to keep you from marrying this gold digger!' Josephine said.

'I thought it was something like that,' Scarlett said. 'But they won't believe that story in the ladies' lounge, Mother Babcock.'

'Why not?'

'I'll tell you why, Josephine,' Hot Lips said. 'Because when Abdullah told Hiram here he'd like to do something nice for the young folks, like give them a couple of oil wells, Hiram told him he didn't have to. Scarlett's got a couple of her own oil wells.'

'Three hundred and eleven, actually,' Scarlett said. 'Not counting Alaska.'

'My dear,' Josephine said. 'Can you ever forgive me? I was only doing my mother's duty as I saw that duty!'

'Probably not,' Scarlett said. 'But if you work hard at it, over the years, you can probably work your way back into my good graces.'

'How could I do that?'

'You can start by getting back to the motel and helping Stanley with the Polish wedding feast,' Bubba said. 'Just as soon as we get back there, Scarlett and I are going to be joined together in holy wedlock.'

'You're sure you can get a clergyman on such short notice?'

'What do I look like, Josephine?' Hot Lips snapped. 'The neighbourhood witch doctor?'

'Forgive me!' Josephine said. 'I'll get right back to the motel.'

Josephine ran out of the room. Scarlett suddenly felt bad.

'Uncle Hiram,' she said. 'Go after her, and tell her I was only kidding.'

'Go after her yourself,' Uncle Hiram replied. 'I'm looking for my little prairie flower.'

His little prairie flower, at that moment, dressed in a fresh, stiffly starched uniform, appeared in the corridor as Josephine ran down it. Wherever the lady was bound, Esther decided, was obviously the site of the emergency. She ran after her.

'Speaking of prairie flowers, Hiram,' Hot Lips said, 'yours just ran down the corridor.'

Hiram ran after her.

Don Rhotten, meanwhile, was waiting in ambush outside the hospital. As four sturdy technicians kept Teddy Roosevelt from marching into the hospital after Scarlett, and Taylor P. Jambon stirred the *soja hispida Babcockisis* with which they were going to poison Teddy Roosevelt, Don Rhotten explained, via satellite, to all his viewers out there in TV Land, what was about to happen. Henri Flambeau, deep in concentration, already wearing his doggie-doctor jacket, marched back and forth repeating his lines.

Josephine Babcock appeared at the hospital door.

'And there she is, ladies and gentlemen,' Don Rhotten said. 'Josephine Babcock, herself, coming to you live via satellite.' He rushed up to her and stuck the microphone under her nose.

'Tell me, Mrs Babcock,' he snarled. 'Are you familiar with *soja hispida Babcockisis*? Answer yes or no.'

'Of course, I am,' she said. 'What is this, anyway?'

Esther Flanagan burst out of the door.

'What the hell is going on here, anyway?' she demanded. 'Where's the medical emergency?'

'Be patient, we're getting to that,' Don Rhotten said.

'Do you feed this foul substance to innocent buffaloes? Answer yes or no.'

'I don't,' Josephine said, truthfully. 'I have people who do that sort of thing for me.'

'You were supposed to answer yes or no,' Don Rhotten said. 'Would it surprise you to know that I have a supply of *soja hispida Babcockisis*, and a real-life buffalo right here with me?'

'You look vaguely familiar,' Josephine replied. 'Are you Howard K. Smith?'

'No, I'm not Howard K. Smith,' Don Rhotten replied, angrily. 'I'm Don Rhotten.'

'Who?'

'Don Rhotten.'

'Never heard of you,' she said.

'You can't say that to me!' he said.

'Why not? Now get out of my way,' she said.

'Taylor, quick,' Don Rhotten called. 'Feed the buffalo the stuff.'

The camera moved to Taylor P. Jambon and his container of *soja hispida Babcockisis*. Mr Jambon put it in front of Teddy Roosevelt. Teddy Roosevelt's mouth opened, his tongue came out, he inhaled, and the bucket was empty. Teddy then indicated he wanted more by mooing at Mr Jambon. Mr Jambon fled.

Uncle Hiram walked out of the hospital, spotted Esther and walked up to her.

Henri Flambeau had his cue. He stepped up before the cameras. 'Never in my extensive veterinary practice,' he solemnly intoned, 'which has taken me to the far corners . . .'

'Henri Flambeau,' Esther said. 'You're a liar and a cheat!'

'Is that the Frenchman who tried to steal your heart, my little prairie flower?' Uncle Hiram asked.

'That's the lousy Frenchman, all right,' Esther said. 'But what's this my little prairie flower business?'